# National Conformity Assessment Schemes

# National Conformity Assessment Schemes

Nontariff Trade Barriers
in Information Technology

**Authors**

William B. Garrison Jr.
Peter S. Watson

**November 1999**

# About CSIS

**The Center for Strategic and International Studies (CSIS),** established in 1962, is a private, tax-exempt institution focusing on international public policy issues. Its research is nonpartisan and nonproprietary.

CSIS is dedicated to policy impact. It seeks to inform and shape selected policy decisions in government and the private sector to meet the increasingly complex and difficult global challenges that leaders will confront in the next century. It achieves this mission in four ways: by generating strategic analysis that is anticipatory and interdisciplinary; by convening policymakers and other influential parties to assess key issues; by building structures for policy action; and by developing leaders.

CSIS does not take specific public policy positions. Accordingly, all views, positions, and conclusions expressed in this publication should be understood to be solely those of the authors.

Library of Congress Cataloging-in-Publication Data
CIP information available upon request.

ISBN: 0-89206-361-0

**The CSIS Press**
Center for Strategic and International Studies
1800 K Street, N.W., Washington, D.C. 20006
Telephone: (202) 887-0200
Fax: (202) 775-3199
E-mail: books@csis.org
Web site: http://www.csis.org/

# Contents

# Preface

The Center for Strategic and International Studies (CSIS) has undertaken a project to evaluate options for the development of a global approach to product regulation for information and telecommunications technology and equipment. This project is a part of ongoing work, conducted by the International Communications Program at CSIS, assessing effects of nontraditional trade barriers on the expanding global economy. Among those barriers are product regulations.

This report examines product regulations now applied to information technologies (IT), specifically focusing on testing, certification, and conformity assessment. As the global demand for IT products expands—stimulated increasingly by the effects of the newWorldTrade Organization (WTO) agreements on information technologies, basic telecommunications services, and financial services—the market-retardant effects of product regulations in this sector will be heightened.

This study is conducted in conjunction with the InformationTechnology Industry Council (ITI). ITI is a Washington, D.C., association that represents leading IT companies. ITI has identified standards, testing, certification, and conformity assessment measures as being among the most important obstacles to trade in IT products and services. The study is not concerned with private standards making versus government standards making but rather with a twofold question: How is conformity to given standards, regardless of method of promulgation, assessed by regulators, and how do current conformity assessment schemes affect the global market for IT products and services?

This report examines the trade effects of national conformity assessment regulations on IT products. Options for eliminating unnecessary regulation are identified and a global approach to conformity assessment is proposed to maximize self-regulation by industry consistent with legitimate public policy concerns related to health, safety, and consumer protection.

The International Communications Program has a long track record of assisting policymakers in analyzing and addressing market and policy challenges resulting from the dramatic changes taking place in the information and telecommunications industries. In keeping with that tradition, International Communications has conducted this study with the participation of an industry working group composed of representatives of major companies in these industries.

During the past several years, the International Communications Program has been engaged in evaluating the impact of the changing information and telecommunications environment on developing, as well as industrialized, economies. An important element of this project on product regulation is a focus on the needs and opportunities of developing economies in the global information services marketplace. This report consequently reflects particular concern with the economic stakes of developing countries relative to testing, certification, and conformity assessment of IT products.

International Communications wishes to acknowledge the important contributions to this study made by the staff and leadership of ITI and the companies participating in working groups.

## ITI Staff

Rhett Dawson
*President*

John Godfrey
*Director, Technology Policy*

Oliver R. Smoot
*Executive Vice President*

Connie Correll
*Director, Communications*

Kathryn Hauser
*Vice President, International Trade*

## ITI Member Companies

3Com Corporation
Apple Computer, Inc.
Cisco Systems, Inc.
Compaq Computer Corporation
Dell Computer Corporation
Eastman Kodak Company
Gateway
Hewlett-Packard Company
Hitachi Computer Products
    (America), Inc.
IBM Corporation
Intel Corporation
Lexmark International, Inc.
Microsoft Corporation

Mitsubishi Electronics America
Motorola, Inc.
NCR Corporation
Panasonic Communications and
    Systems Company
Pitney Bowes Inc.
SGI
Sony Electronics Inc.
StorageTek
Symbol Technologies, Inc.
Tektronix, Inc.
Tyco International (US) Inc.
Unisys Corporation
Xerox Corporation

The authors wish to express thanks to the following additional individuals for their expert commentary and contributions.

David Adams
*Hewlett-Packard Company*

David Lyng
*Hewlett-Packard Company*

George Arnold
*Lucent Technologies, Inc.*

William Maxwell
*Hewlett-Packard Company*

Steve M. Crosby
*Lucent Technologies, Inc.*

Allen Miller
*EDS*

T. A. (Ted) Heydinger
*Dell Computer Corporation*

John S. Wilson
*World Bank*

Richard Holleman
*IBM Corporation*

# Executive Summary

The global market for information technology (IT) products is undergoing radical alteration. Fundamental changes in information and telecommunications technologies are transforming the nature of these products, lowering production costs, and driving rapidly accelerating market demand. That demand, however, will be greatly constrained by current systems of conformity assessment that govern entry and deployment of IT into many national markets.

Many conformity assessment systems were designed during an era characterized by long product life; relatively low levels of technological innovation and product differentiation; and pervasive regulatory control over essential facilities, notably public telephone networks. None of these conditions now characterize today's fast changing IT sector. As a result, traditional conformity assessment systems are outmoded and cannot keep pace with technological innovations.

In an increasing number of countries, conformity is required with national standards that are unique to a given national market. Even where international standards apply, manufacturers and suppliers are required by individual national schemes to demonstrate repeatedly that products conform to those identical standards. Thus national schemes create economic barriers and delay products reaching the market.

Where national conformity assessment requirements and processes extend the period for approval to time spans that represent significant percentages of product life, manufacturers and consumers alike suffer economic harm through increased costs and delayed availability of both equipment and related services. Separate national schemes increase costs to both manufacturers and consumers, constrain technological deployment, and restrict consumer choice.

Proliferating national schemes constitute a brake on the phenomenal growth that both information and telecommunications technology companies are experiencing. At a time when the global telecommunications and information services market is moving toward deregulation, a concerted parallel movement needs to be undertaken by makers of public policy to liberalize market entry for related equipment.

The success of regulatory reform of conformity assessment schemes on a global scale will depend on governments supporting two fundamental concepts: the first is accepting international standards, not separate national standards, for IT products; the other is moving to *ex post* regulation of these products.

## *Ex Ante* versus *Ex Post* Regulation

Regulatory intervention in economic markets generally takes two forms—*ex ante* and *ex post*. *Ex ante* systems of regulation apply rules of entry and behavior before market entry and generally are prescriptive in placing obligations on potential market participants. *Ex post* systems apply regulation after entry with penalties for behavior deemed to be illegal or to violate applicable regulations. Conformity assessment schemes are *ex ante* in nature.

An increasing number of IT products are becoming integrated into the provision of converged communication and information services. As technological convergence accelerates, IT products are at risk of being subjected to national *ex ante* requirements applied to equipment used in the provision of regulated services.

At the same time, IT products increasingly conform to international standards and are increasingly fungible in multiple markets regardless of national variations in standards. The regulatory trend toward increased national conformity schemes contradicts the trend toward international standards in IT products.

A major weakness of *ex ante* regulation of IT products in this new environment is that certifying agents, whether government agencies or independent third parties, are often unable to process approvals in a timely fashion. *Ex post* regulation can eliminate or substantially reduce entry delays and can greatly lower costs added by *ex ante* schemes.

*Ex post* regulation is both more flexible and more efficient in that it permits all players to respond to market demands according to their individual capabilities and applies corrective measures only to "bad actors" in cases of actual violation of laws or regulations in the course of marketplace behavior. *Ex ante* conformity assessment schemes, however, unduly burden all market participants, whether bad actors or not.

A system of *ex post* regulation for IT products would not mean that conformity assessment would have no role. Most elements that compose current *ex ante* systems of conformity assessment could be utilized in *ex post* regulation. Consistent with an *ex post* scheme, governments could require manufacturers and suppliers to file relevant conformity information at the time a product clears custom or at pre-entry registration. Self-declaration of conformity, now in common use in this sector, should be sufficient to fulfill such a requirement.

## The At-Risk Position of Small Companies and Developing Economies

For small and medium-sized enterprises, national conformity assessment schemes are, arguably, the most significant export barrier and are the single largest source of cost to them when they do attempt to export. Small firms cannot absorb the cost of multiple national requirements and, thus, are effectively barred from participating in the increasingly globalized IT marketplace.

Developing countries that restrict or do not facilitate the entry of new IT products into their markets are at risk of falling behind in the economic growth that is driven by information and communication services. By creating these conformity assessment requirements, governments endanger the ability of their economies to participate fully in the global economy. Without state-of-the-art equipment, service providers in these sectors are hampered in meeting current and future demand.

## Developing a Global Approach to Conformity Assessment

Several options for developing a global approach to conformity assessment have been identified during the course of this study. They are

- mutual recognition agreements,

- unilateral acceptance,

- one-stop shopping,

- best practices and benchmarking, and

- a global framework of principles.

We believe that the options through which this change may best be implemented are the last two above: best practices and a global framework of principles. These two options should not be seen as mutually exclusive. A global framework of principles could be agreed upon by governments through current Information Technology Agreement (ITA) talks or by modification of the Agreement on Technical Barriers to Trade (TBT). Implementation of those principles could be supported by industry through a best-practices analysis that would provide guidance concerning ways in which conformity requirements can be efficiently met and that would also serve as benchmarks for governments in assessing industry compliance.

To assist regulators in verifying information set forth in conformity declarations, particularly during the conduct of a compliance review, company-maintained databases or InternetWeb sites should be encouraged. Third-party certifiers should be required to file test data based on a common format that could support elimination of separate certification. Eventually regulators and custom officials should accept electronic filing of declarations to facilitate market entry and to minimize variations in information disclosures.

# Statement of Issues

The IT and telecommunications equipment industry has become one of the most important sectors of the global economy. The world market for these products and components in 1997 amounted to $1.1 trillion.[1]

The global climate for these products is undergoing radical change. Advances in information and telecommunications technologies are transforming the nature of these products, lowering production costs, and driving rapidly accelerating market demand.

This convergence is occurring at the same time that a new era in global liberalization for this sector has begun with the adoption of the WTO agreements on information technologies and on telecommunications services. As the nations that collectively constitute almost the entire global market for telecommunications services open their national markets to competitive provision of these services, the demand for telecommunications and IT products—the vehicles for providing these services—is certain to increase at an unprecedented rate.

The first Information Technology Agreement (ITA) has been successful in eliminating tariffs on a wide range of IT products. A second round of talks, ITA II, has commenced. An overriding goal of these negotiations is to make the benefits of global information infrastructure available worldwide more quickly and less expensively. The work conducted under the ITA rubric has produced a definition of IT that includes a broad scope of products such as computers, peripherals, telecommunications equipment, software, and semiconductors. For most of these product categories, market-entry approval is required by many countries.

Remaining trade barriers to be tackled are the current national systems of conformity assessment that govern the entry and deployment of information and telecommunications technology products into national markets. The procedure by which products are determined to comply with standards and other regulatory requirements is known as conformity assessment. Conformity assessment usually involves some combination of the following procedures:

- Testing of products and components by independent laboratories;

- Formal certification of conformity;

- Independent audit and approval of quality manufacturing systems leading to registration with a quality systems registrar; and

- Manufacturer's self-declaration of conformity through its own testing systems.

---

1. U.S. International Trade Commission, *Global Assessment of Standards Barriers to Trade in the Information Technology Industry,* Staff Research Study 23, Publication 3141 (Washington, D.C.: GPO, November 1998), 2-1.

In many countries, a particular product can be sold in a given national market only after the relevant government regulatory agency or agencies have accepted the assessment. Under this form of regulation, manufacturers are usually required to have their products tested to determine if the products comply with relevant standards and, then, to have the test results and conformity to applicable standards certified, usually by a government agency or an independent testing body. In some situations, however, a manufacturer is allowed to make use of internal procedures to test and to establish compliance.

These conformity assessment systems were designed in an era that was characterized by long product life, relatively low levels of technological innovation and product differentiation, and pervasive regulatory control over essential facilities, notably public telecommunications networks. None of these conditions now characterizes today's fast changing information and telecommunications technology sector.

In the past, IT products and telecommunications equipment were subject to fundamentally different product regulation schemes. The telecommunications industry traditionally has been pervasively regulated, either through government oversight or through government ownership. As an extension of general regulatory policy toward telecommunications providers, telecommunications equipment has been subject to prescriptive requirements regarding health and safety concerns, electromagnetic emissions, and operability. Conformity assessment of telecommunications equipment has long been common in developed markets and is becoming increasingly so in developing economies.

Information technology products, in contrast, have been either unregulated or regulated under comparatively cursory regimes with safety and noninterference generally being the regulatory focus. However, IT products are increasingly subjected to product regulation schemes modeled on or derived from the regulatory schemes applied to telecommunications equipment.

With the increase in technological convergence now manifest in both the telecommunications and information sectors, there is increasing danger that IT products will be subjected to greater product regulation than has been the case in the past, with no indication that such an increased burden is justified. At the same time, telecommunications equipment liberalization may not move forward at a pace that will be responsive to market demands generated by expanding communication and information service competition. At a time when the global telecommunications services market is moving toward deregulation, a concerted, parallel movement needs to be undertaken by public policymakers toward liberalization of market entry for related equipment.

A recent report of the International Trade Commission (ITC), a U.S. government agency, noted that many emerging economies in Asia, Latin America, and the former Soviet bloc countries are in the process of developing and implementing individual national standards for this industry.[2] These national standards give rise to regulatory requirements placed on manufacturers and suppliers to demonstrate that the products they propose to sell conform to those national standards. Many

2.  Ibid., 3-19.

companies will not incur the additional cost to manufacture products that would conform to such national standards just to be able to sell in these individual markets. Consumers, therefore, in those countries may be deprived of technologies and products needed to participate fully in the global economy.

The more common case arises where countries have imposed separate national regimes to establish conformity with international standards.[3] The national profiles contained in appendix A illustrate this situation. For manufacturers, the obligation to meet multiple national assessment requirements just to demonstrate conformity to the same standards represents a significant cost burden and substantially delays market entry and product deployment as well.

Many new IT products are now considered obsolete within 24 months after their introduction.[4] Where national conformity assessment requirements and processes extend the period for approval to time spans that represent significant percentages of product life, manufacturers and consumers alike suffer economic harm through increased costs and delayed availability of both equipment and related services.

The negative market effects of separate national schemes are an increased cost to both manufacturers and consumers, unnecessary constraint on technological deployment, and restriction on consumer choice. The increasing number of national conformity assessment regimes constitutes a brake on the phenomenal growth that both information and telecommunications technology companies are experiencing. Because the information and communications industry, broadly understood, is now deemed by policymakers, public and private, to be one of the principal engines of economic growth, any constraint on its ability to fulfill that promise must be deemed, on its face, a matter of priority concern.

---

3. Ibid., 3-9.
4. Ibid., 4-2.

# CHAPTER 2

# Public Policy Concerns and Regulatory Responses

Conformity assessment schemes have evolved in most instances as regulatory responses to legitimate public policy concerns. In the case of IT products, policy concerns are primarily related to consumer safety, electromagnetic emissions, and compatibility at the interface between a given product and communications networks, primarily the public switched telephone network.

In the case of telecommunications products, however, other policy concerns arise. Telecommunications equipment has to be certified as conforming with national standards that govern interoperability and, in some cases, integration with the public switched telephone network. Although conformity assessment of telecommunications equipment also reaches concerns about safety (for both workers and consumers) and electromagnetic emissions, those products must also conform with requirements that address harm to the public network as well as environmental effects in certain cases.

These policy concerns historically have been addressed in the context of national markets. This national approach has been and, in certain cases, remains appropriate to telecommunications equipment because of the variations dictated by the national or regional technical standards that apply to telephone networks. However, the IT industry differs importantly from the telecommunications industry in that IT product manufacturers generally conform to international standards. These manufacturers meet policy concerns regarding safety and electromagnetic emissions by complying with international standards that address these matters. Conformity with such international standards should mean that national variations in conformity assessment requirements for IT products provide little or no additional value in terms of achieving those public policy goals.

The manner in which national governments have addressed these policy concerns should be considered in the larger context of traditional regulatory theory. Regulatory intervention in economic markets generally takes two forms—*ex ante* and *ex post*. *Ex ante* systems of regulation make use of rules of entry and behavior before market entry and generally are prescriptive in placing obligations on potential market participants. They require prior compliance with regulatory requirements and often require approvals that certify such compliance before market entry is granted. Traditional U.S. public utility regulation is an example of highly developed and differentiated *ex ante* regulation of both market entry and subsequent market activity of approved service providers.

*Ex post* systems apply regulation after entry with penalties for behavior deemed to be illegal or to violate applicable regulations. Manufacturers and vendors of consumer products in the United States and in many other countries have been traditionally subject to *ex post* regulation. Antitrust (or competition) regulation and product liability laws are examples of *ex post* regulation.

In many areas of economic activity, participants are subject to both *ex ante* and *ex post* regulatory requirements. The pharmaceutical industry, for example, has traditionally been subject to extensive *ex ante* approvals for drugs or product lines as well as subject to *ex post* consumer protection and product liability regulation.

The telecommunications industry, in terms of both equipment and services, has traditionally been subject to pervasive *ex ante* and *ex post* regulation. That regulation has generally taken the form of either quasi-judicial regulatory processes as is the case in the United States and Canada, for example, or less formal management review and control through state ownership or state direction as was the case in Japan and the European Union countries until recently and as remains the case in many developing countries.

Conformity assessment for telecommunications equipment can be seen as having been consistent with the traditional *ex ante* regulation broadly applied to the entire telecommunications sector. Regulatory approval before market entry was arguably appropriate to the relatively static market characteristics and the lengthy depreciation environments that have been hallmarks of the telecommunications industry for much of its history. IT products, on the other hand, have not been subject to significant *ex ante* requirements as they were not viewed as integral to the provision of regulated services.

In today's environment, however, IT products increasingly conform to international standards and are increasingly fungible in multiple markets regardless of national variations in standards. The regulatory trend toward increased national conformity schemes contradicts the trend in IT products toward international standards. At the same time, many IT products are becoming more integrated into the provision of converged services. As technological convergence accelerates, IT products are at risk of being subjected to national *ex ante* requirements applied to equipment used in the provision of regulated services.

*Ex post* regulation can eliminate or substantially reduce market-entry delays and greatly lower costs added by national conformity assessment schemes. A major weakness of *ex ante* regulation in the new environment for IT products is that certifying agents, whether government agencies or independent third parties, are often unable to process approvals in a timely fashion.

*Ex post* regulation is both more flexible and more efficient than pre-entry approvals in that it permits all participants to respond to market demands according to their individual capabilities and applies corrective measures only to so-called bad actors in cases of actual violation of laws or regulations in the course of marketplace behavior. *Ex ante* conformity assessment schemes, however, unduly burden all market participants, whether bad actors or not.

# CHAPTER 3

# National Conformity Assessment Requirements— Examples

In the course of conducting this study, International Communications at CSIS undertook comparative examinations of conformity assessment requirements in various countries. The national schemes in Chile, Australia, New Zealand, and Taiwan were selected for inclusion in this report because, taken together, they give a reasonably complete the range of *ex ante* and *ex post* regulatory requirements to be found in national schemes around the world. Four country profiles are set forth in appendix A.

These national profiles provide detailed descriptions of the requirements and processes entailed in testing, certification, and conformity assessment in each of the four countries.

These countries provide a continuum from highly liberalized to highly regulated market entry for IT products. Chile is the least regulatory in its requirements, while Taiwan provides an example of a highly regulatory *ex ante* system of approvals. Australia and New Zealand are taken together because they have achieved substantial harmonization and liberalization on a bilateral basis. In the course of the development of a joint approach, Australia has gone from a system primarily made up of traditional *ex ante* approvals to a more liberalized system. New Zealand, in contrast, has adopted additional regulatory requirements in certain instances in order to implement joint procedures.

Chile imposes virtually no conformity assessment requirements on IT and limits such standards, testing, and certification for telecommunications equipment to requirements deemed necessary to protect network interoperability. Chile relies heavily on international standards; where national standards are imposed, they are generally in line with related international or regional standards. Even though Chile does not accept declarations of conformity (DOCs) by manufacturers or suppliers, entry into the Chilean market is relatively unrestricted. Chile is attempting to develop mutual recognition agreements (MRAs), addressing certification and accreditation requirements, with several countries. However, MRAs have proved difficult to achieve because few countries have been willing to adopt conformity assessment schemes as liberal and as open as Chile's.

Australia and New Zealand have developed a high level of integration of their national requirements. They both promote industry self-regulation through voluntary codes and standards. In most instances they have developed joint standards that comply, for the most part, with applicable international standards or suites of standards. Both use independent nonprofit organizations to promulgate voluntary joint standards and thereby allow substantial industry involvement in standards setting. Manufacturers and suppliers are required to evidence conformity in only one country in order to do business in both.

Accreditation of laboratories is coordinated through a joint intergovernmental organization. A laboratory that is formally registered with its home country's scheme will be jointly recognized if the home country scheme is acceptable to the either Australia's or New Zealand's regulator. The selection of a testing laboratory is left to a manufacturer or a supplier and is not dictated by either government. Self-testing is allowed for all equipment.

The use of the DOC varies between the two countries. In Australia, the DOC is used in conjunction with a compliance folder (CF) and related marks. The DOC must be held in Australia, but other elements of the CF may be held outside the country after the elements been examined and approved. In New Zealand, however, a manufacturer or supplier is deemed to have made a self-declaration regarding safety requirements by merely offering equipment for sale on the market. A DOC is required of the marketing organization on an individual-product basis in the event of incident or complaint. In the area of electromagnetic compatibility (EMC) compliance, the new joint arrangement deems a product declared in one market to be declared in both. Both countries perform random postentry audits but will exempt from such an audit any element that is covered by pre-entry third-party conformity assessment.

Taiwan uses a traditional, pervasive system of before-entry conformity assessment that restricts the ability of foreign manufacturers to sell products in a timely manner. The government has an explicit policy of promoting foreign market entry for Taiwanese companies and uses technical standards as a tool in promoting such entry for Taiwanese IT manufacturers. Cooperation with international accreditation and testing bodies is undertaken to assist domestic manufacturers in gaining entry into overseas markets, not to promote liberalized entry into Taiwan.

Standards are tightly controlled by the government with very little industry participation in standards setting. All equipment, including computers and peripherals, must meet safety and EMC standards. All equipment must be certified by Taiwanese testing laboratories designated by the government; they cannot be selected by the manufacturer or the supplier. Test reports and owner manuals must be in Chinese and must be submitted for review and approval before certification will be considered. Certification must be completed before any equipment can clear custom and be marketed.

In the case of equipment that cannot be tested by a Taiwanese testing laboratory, overseas testing must be supervised by Taiwanese officials—a time-consuming process at its best. Labeling is compulsory but is allowed only when the manufacturer has established a quality assurance system approved by the government. Products cannot be offered on the market until labeling has been attached.

# CHAPTER 4

# Global Approach to Conformity Assessment Needed

As the country profiles indicate, conformity assessment schemes are characterized by a substantial degree of variability in requirements and procedures. The necessity for manufacturers to conform to these variable factors increases the cost of production and marketing with little or no value derived from such additional costs. The increasing global demand for IT products exacerbates the negative economic effects of these national variations as an increasing number of products are demanded by an enlarging consumer public.

Globalization has moved trade issues to the forefront of the international policy agenda. By undermining national regulatory sovereignty, globalization has blurred the distinction between trade policy and health, safety, and environmental regulation.[5] The issues addressed by conformity assessment have traditionally been regarded as national in focus. However, as IT products become much more international in their technical standards and in the markets they address, reassessment is required of the trade effects of national conformity assessment schemes as applied to IT products. What is required is a more efficient method of conformity assessment through which legitimate domestic policy concerns can be met while broad policy goals of trade promotion and economic growth can be facilitated.

Because IT manufacturers design to international standards, measures taken by these manufacturers and suppliers to comply with national conformity assessment requirements are often more expensive than the actual conformity to standards. Even though IT manufacturers conform to the same international standards that apply across all national markets, they are compelled to demonstrate that conformity in each individual country. Thus the cost imposed on IT manufacturers and suppliers by repeated testing, inspection, audit, and other procedures necessary to meet national conformity assessment requirements far exceeds benefits to the manufacturer, the regulator, or the consumer.[6]

---

5. David Vogel, "Regulatory Cooperation between the European Union and the United States," *ECSA Review* (Summer 1997): 4.

6. U.S. International Trade Commission, *Global Assessment of Standards Barriers*, 3-5; and John S. Wilson, "Triennial Review of the Agreement on Technical Barriers to Trade," (paper presented at experts briefing at meeting of the World Trade Organization, Geneva, Switzerland, April 18, 1998), 1–2.

When national regulations affect the competitive position and relative cost of market share of foreign producers vis-à-vis domestic ones, they move from the area of a country's own business into the sphere of international relations.[7] Where conformity assessment requirements are used to protect domestic stakeholders or where they have the effect of excluding or retarding market entry by foreign competitors, they fail to serve legitimate domestic regulatory goals and give rise to trade policy concerns. These trade concerns elevate domestic policy considerations related to conformity assessment to international concerns.

In this context, the nontariff trade barrier of most significance is compliance with multiple national regimes when identical international standards apply in each national scheme.[8] Moreover, the specification of national standards that differ from international standards exacerbates time delays and increases process costs for market entry, making such national conformity assessment requirements even more uneconomic and, in some cases, anticompetitive.

The position of developing countries is of particular concern. Although our findings apply to all countries and participants in the industry, developing countries have the most to gain from liberalized market entry for information and telecommunications technology products and, concomitantly, the most to lose by unnecessarily restrictive schemes. Economies with open and flexible market entry for suppliers of both equipment and services have greater chance for success in the era of globalization as these economies stand to gain substantial competitive advantages by quickly capturing the benefits of technological innovation. Countries that restrict entry or do not facilitate the entry of new providers and products into their markets are at risk of falling behind in an overall economic growth that is increasingly driven by information and communication services.

In newly industrialized and developing countries, policy priorities relative to this industry vary substantially. Nations with indigenous or incipient manufacturers often use product regulation as a nontariff trade barrier with which to protect the domestic market position of their manufacturers or entrepreneurs. Other nations that do not have such domestic constituencies are more likely to have product regulation schemes that might not unduly restrict product entry.

In many cases, the national markets of developing countries are too small to supply a technological and economic base sufficient to enable their IT industry to achieve technological leadership. Protectionist barriers contribute to a lack of incentive to innovate on the part of protected companies by insulating them from the stimulus of competitive pressure from external sources and allowing them, at the same time, to resist responding to demands for innovation from their domestic customer base.

In this industry, however, technological innovation is key to survival and expansion. To the degree that product regulation depresses innovation on the part of indigenous companies in developing economies, it places an unacceptable burden on such protected companies by insuring that they will be unfit to compete in export markets and will ultimately fail. Moreover, protectionist product regulation

---

7. Vogel, "Regulatory Cooperation," 4.
8. U.S. International Trade Commission, *Global Assessment of Standards Barriers,* 5-1.

schemes designed to help a few in one sector damage industries and enterprises in other sectors that depend on the availability of information products and services.

For countries with no domestic IT industry, the negative effects of costly, duplicative conformity assessment requirements are arguably the greatest because even limited economic gains for a protected few do not exist. Governments in such countries that adopt these schemes endanger the overall ability of their economies to participate rapidly and fully in the burgeoning sectors of economic activity that require advanced communication and information services and technologies.

# CHAPTER 5

# Options for Achieving a Global Approach

During the course of this study, we have identified several options for developing a global approach to conformity assessment. These options are examined below with particular consideration given to whether they would perpetuate existing *ex ante* regulatory schemes or whether they would support adoption of liberalizing *ex post* schemes.

## Mutual Recognition Agreements

Mutual recognition agreements (MRAs) represent a government-to-government approach to ameliorating the problems that arise from divergent national product regulation schemes. These agreements are premised on mutual acceptance by participating countries of existing requirements. They do not necessarily result i harmonization of divergent requirements or in the elimination or substantial reduction of unnecessary regulation in a given market.

They require instead that regulators in a given country to accept another country's processes when they qualify products for sale in their respective national markets. The regulatory requirements of the participating countries remain in place. Because in most cases MRAs essentially validate traditional product regulation, they continue existing *ex ante* schemes.

The MRA process binds only the negotiating parties. Because MRAs are currently being negotiated on a bilateral basis or in the context of regional markets or trading blocs, they are not likely to provide an efficient or timely process for achieving global agreement on a new regulatory regime for IT products.

Some observers believe MRAs work best in ameliorating the market barrier effects of national standards schemes in industries such as telecommunications that have traditionally been subject to pervasive regulation.[9] In such cases, multiple MRAs, although they permit divergent national requirements, can result in a diminution of the number of conformity assessment schemes to which a given manufacturer must comply. To that extent, bilateral or regional MRAs represent a positive breakthrough in reducing some of the trade barrier effects of separate national schemes.

The trade policy goal for IT products, however, should not simply be mutual recognition of the individual national schemes on the part of various trading

---

9. Ibid., 5-3.

partners. Nor should it be achievement of a harmonized set of *ex ante* regulations mutually applied, particularly where those regulations continue economic inefficiencies. Instead, a more fundamental shift to *ex post* regulation of IT products should be pursued.

## Unilateral Acceptance

Unilateral acceptance is a derivative of the traditional most-favored-nation (MFN) principle. Under this option, any given country on its own initiative could extend MFN recognition to national schemes that are based on international guides and standards.

This approach does not require negotiation, either bilateral or multilateral. A country is free to extend this treatment to any other nation whose scheme is deemed to conform to relevant standards. Where international standards apply, unilateral acceptance is a positive approach. Unilateral acceptance would mean that the conformity assessment procedures used in a given country (to establish that IT products conform to accepted international standards) would be recognized by another country as valid for the purposes of granting certification to the same products in its market.

The strength of this approach is the speed of adoption that it permits a country intent on liberalizing its domestic market. However, unilateral acceptance does not counter the ability of countries to adopt local variations that can have market-barrier or market-retardant effects nor does it provide a way forward in accomplishing reform on a global basis. Although this option would significantly reduce the cost and time burdens of entry into a given second market, it would not necessarily promote a reduction of assessment requirements placed on manufacturers domiciled within a given national market for products to be sold in that market. Moreover, this approach could serve to promulgate either *ex ante* or *ex post* regulation according to the nature of the national schemes in question and, therefore, does not ensure that the needed reform in conformity assessment regulation will be achieved.

## One-Stop Shopping

This option contemplates a system based on a common certification process—recognized as sufficient for use in all markets—that a manufacturer would undergo only once. The key attribute is testing and certification by independent third parties whose competence is recognized by all governments.

The principal weakness of this option, from the perspective of this study, is that it would essentially constitute a broad system of *ex ante* conformity assessment. Although a global approach, it would not achieve the efficiencies and economies to be gained by *ex post* regulation of IT products.

# Best Practices and Benchmarking

This option could be led by industry through the development of a set of recommended "best practices" for conformity assessment drawn from current national schemes. Those practices could then be used as benchmarks for governments against which to measure and reform individual national schemes. They could also be used by trade negotiators as benchmarks against which to evaluate proposals for formal agreements that address conformity assessment between or among nations.

A best-practices approach could incorporate elements of either *ex ante* or *ex post* systems according to individual standards or regulatory elements. However, economic efficiency should dictate that in most cases the best practice identified should be one that is appropriate to an *ex post* regulatory environment.

If governments adhere to most or all identified practices, a substantial degree of commonality among national schemes could be achieved. In cases where governments are using individual national schemes for protectionism, however, benchmarking provides inadequate incentives for them to adopt reforms. Moreover, this option provides no enforceable remedy against a given country adopting individual national standards.

# A Global Framework of Principles

Another multilateral approach is the adoption of general regulatory principles for conformity assessment; all participating governments would be bound to the principles. For example, the Agreement on Trade in Basic Telecommunications Services incorporates a set of regulatory principles that most countries bound by that agreement are obligated to follow. These principles provide a useful precedent because they set out the fundamental regulatory processes and standards that are required of countries to conform with the obligations undertaken to open up national markets to competitive provision of telecommunications services.

Incorporation of a similar framework of conformity assessment regulatory principles could be undertaken as a function of the ITA II discussions, with the goal of enshrining such principles in the ITA. This approach is also reflected in the fundamental principles set out in the Agreement on Technical Barriers to Trade (TBT); these principles might be expanded to provide a similar framework to govern conformity assessment schemes. Either the ITA II or the TBT offers the opportunity to bring the framework principles into the WTO, to then be enforced through the formal trade dispute resolution process.

A more informal process might allow an alternative to the WTO agreements. During 1998–1999, the United States, the European Union and Japan have been moving toward acceptance of a common framework to guide the development of electronic commerce. A similar initiative could be undertaken by those or other nations to move forward on a framework for conformity assessment that would apply at least to the largest national or regional markets. A major weakness of this approach is that developing countries that have implemented national compliance assessment schemes would not be addressed. In the case of developing countries that have no *ex ante* conformity assessment requirements, the international trade policy community should encourage them not to adopt such schemes. In view of the trend toward adoption of *ex ante* product regulation among those countries, a process with limited participants may not provide an adequate or timely path to a global scheme.

A risk that exists in the use of any such framework is that the agreed principles may be too broad or too general. Also, they might address only the lowest common denominator of agreement and, thus, allow unacceptable levels of variation in regulations among participating countries. Moreover, principles, in and of themselves, might give insufficient guidance to national regulators and might permit individual national schemes that incorporate inefficient and burdensome elements.

Regardless of the process used to reach agreement, such a framework should articulate the imperative of moving to *ex post* regulation; otherwise, the framework could serve to validate *ex ante* systems that would perpetuate identified problems. To support true reform, a fundamental principle must be the adherence by participating nations to international standards for the manufacture of IT products.

# CHAPTER 6

# Recommendations

IT products increasingly conform to international standards and are increasingly fungible in the multiple markets regardless of national variations in standards. Manufacturers are often obligated to meet multiple national assessment requirements just to demonstrate conformity with international standards.

Although we support and encourage unilateral and bilateral acceptance of conformity assessment reform by individual countries, we view that process as insufficient to reverse the current trend of proliferating national schemes. A global approach to conformity assessment is needed to counter this trend and to relieve the trade-barrier effects of national schemes.

Two fundamental concepts must be embraced by governments in developing any global approach. The first is the acceptance of international standards for IT products in every market, not the imposition of separate national standards. The second is a shift away from traditional *ex ante* approvals to *ex post* regulation of IT products. The highly competitive and volatile nature of the IT marketplace supports minimal pre-entry regulation and should make market surveillance, with punitive actions against bad actors, adequate to protect consumer interests.

Of the options identified during the course of this study for achieving a global approach to conformity assessment, we believe that a broad framework of principles would provide a common baseline for governments to use in reforming their national schemes. At the core of any such framework in support of *ex post* regulation should be the principle of self-declaration of conformity by manufacturers or suppliers and the elimination of national pre-entry conformity assessment requirements. Implementation of those principles could be carried out by industry through the development of a best-practices analysis that would provide both guidance on ways in which requirements can be efficiently met and benchmarks to governments for assessing industry compliance.

CHAPTER 7

# Implementation Issues

## How an *Ex Post* System Would Work

Because *ex post* regulation will facilitate rapid deployment of innovative technologies through timely market entry, governments should allow manufacturers and suppliers increased flexibility in establishing product conformity consistent with after-entry regulation. At the same time, governments have appropriate concern that manufacturers and suppliers be effectively held accountable for conformity. Implementation of *ex post* regulation for IT products will depend upon governments being satisfied that legitimate policy concerns can be adequately addressed under such a regulatory system.

A system of *ex post* regulation for IT products would not mean that conformity assessment would have no role. Most elements that compose current *ex ante* systems of conformity assessment could be used in *ex post* regulation but in ways that would eliminate the trade-barrier effects of duplicative requirements, increased costs, and unnecessary delays. Regulatory tools such as testing, certification, conformity declaration, and audits can be used on an after-entry basis in ways appropriate to a given manufacturer and, thereby, can promote ease and speed of market entry and product deployment.

In our view, the issue is more a matter of when conformity must be demonstrated as opposed to whether or how it is demonstrated. Some countries now require that a manufacturer maintain information establishing conformity in a form accessible to regulators for after-entry audits rather than requiring premarket filing, review, and approval. Thus a manufacturer must, for its own interests, ensure conformity at the time of manufacture but might not be called upon to demonstrate that conformity until after a given product is being sold in the market. We believe that this approach is an example of a best practice for regulators and is completely compatible with effective *ex post* regulation.

## The Central Role of DOC and Third-Party Certification

Consistent with an *ex post* scheme, governments could require manufacturers and suppliers to file relevant conformity information at the time a product clears custom or as pre-entry registration. Self-declaration of conformity should be sufficient to fulfill such a requirement. An advantage of such a declaration is that it reduces costly and time-consuming multiple *ex ante* requirements that add no value to the

16

product; however, it continues the exposure of manufacturers or suppliers to full *ex post* liabilities.

Such declarations should document conformity to applicable international standards or suites of standards. Regulators should not mandate, for entry purposes, independent certification but should allow a manufacturer the option of establishing conformity through third-party testing and certification instead of through internal testing and certification systems. The use of third-party certification may be indicated or incorporated into the disclosure information contained in a declaration filed by a manufacturer or supplier.

Any global framework of principles should address the need for consistency in the information to be disclosed in any declaration or certification of conformity, whether provided by a manufacturer or by a third party. We believe that this requirement would be adequately addressed by requiring any declaration of conformity to reflect the standards set out in ISO/IEC Guide 22[10] Additional specifications regarding matters such as local accountability, delivery of declaration with products, public filing of or physical access to a declaration, required records on compliance, rules governing audits, and so forth, can be developed through the International Organization for Standardization (ISO) and promulgated as international standards.

In regard to EMC, Australia provides a useful approach. Self-declaration by manufacturers is accepted, subject to the right of the government to require a post-entry audit. If a manufacturer has chosen, of its own volition, to obtain conformity assessment from a third party before market entry, any elements in that company's declaration of conformity that have been certified by such an independent authority are exempted from examination during any post-entry audit and are accepted by the government as valid. Thus, third-party certification essentially serves as insurance against the costs and procedural burdens of a later audit. The manufacturer can assume the risk of a regulatory compliance review under self-declaration or can eliminate that risk by making use of third-party certification.

Two legitimate concerns for regulators underlie acceptance of self-declaration of conformity: the first is the credibility of the data disclosed, and the second is whether later products will conform with applicable standards as the tested product is declared to have done. The first concern should be adequately addressed by requiring conformity with ISO/IEC Guide 25.[11] The second concern could be addressed by accepting the declaration of companies deemed to be ISO 9000 compliant.

Although ISO 9000 provides assurance to regulators that manufacturers have in place quality control systems that ensure production of equipment compliant with appropriate standards, it has come under substantial criticism.[120] ISO 9000's "one

10. International Organization for Standardization/International Electrotechnical Commission, "General Criteria for Supplier's Declaration of Conformity" (Geneva: ISO/IEC, 1996).

11. International Organization for Standardization/International Electrotechnical Commission, "General Requirements for the Competence of Calibration and Testing Laboratories" (Geneva: ISO/IEC, 1990).

12. Ibid., 4-3–4-4; and National Research Council, *Standards, Conformity Assessment and Trade into the 21st Century* (Washington, D.C.: National Academy of Sciences, 1995), 78–79.

standard, one audit" feature is a useful and appropriate attribute that should support efficient *ex post* regulation. However, ISO 9000 requirements need to be re-evaluated to eliminate unnecessary or unduly burdensome requirements and to allow self-certification of compliance instead of mandatory third-party certification.

## Considerations Relative to Small and Medium-Sized Manufacturers

Many large manufacturers have developed internal facilities and processes for testing and certification not only to permit self-declaration but, in some cases, to develop revenue sources through serving as testing and certification facilities for other companies. In many instances, however, large manufacturers elect to outsource certification to independent testing laboratories. Thus they are able to choose between the conformity assessment option of self-testing or third-party testing. This choice should be based on business factors and not made in response to artificial cost concerns driven by multiple national assessment requirements.

Many small manufacturers are not similarly positioned. They are unlikely to incur the costs associated with or the capital investment required to develop such internal facilities. They have to incur the cost of third-party certification, even under *ex post* regulation. Although this may seem an undue disadvantage, internal testing capabilities represent a substantial cost of business to companies that elect self-declaration. For a smaller company that manufactures a single line or a limited number of product lines, the cost of third-party certification, particularly when that certification is to international standards and is globally accepted, may be the less costly and burdensome alternative. In any case, testing and certification ultimately constitute a cost of doing business that must be borne in one manner or another by all industry participants.

An additional consideration for small and medium-sized manufacturers, particularly those exporting into unfamiliar foreign markets, is that third-party certification can have a positive economic benefit by serving as a form of market validation in situations where such manufacturers do not enjoy brand-name status. Small manufacturers without name recognition in foreign markets face formidable marketing costs if they are to export successfully.

Electronic commerce on the Internet holds the promise of greatly increased market opportunities for small and medium-sized companies. The Internet provides an instantaneous, inexpensive route to market, whether domestic or foreign. However, the Internet's marketing potential will be decreased if these companies continue to confront the trade barriers of multiple national pre-entry conformity assessment requirements. Where these schemes deny these companies certification and burden their products with undue costs, the potential contribution of the Internet to this aspect of global commerce will be diminished.

## A Key Role for Databases and Web Sites

To assist regulators in verifying information set forth in conformity declarations, particularly during the conduct an audit, company-maintained databases or Internet Web sites can supply information substantiating compliance and can provide first-line information needed for effective market surveillance. Compliance information filed in one jurisdiction could be easily cross-referenced by regulators in another country. Information contained in declarations of conformity would be on file and pertinent data supporting that information could be accessed. Third-party certifiers should be required to file test data based on a common format that could support elimination of separate certification. Regulators and custom officials eventually should accept electronic filing of declarations to facilitate market entry and to minimize variations in information disclosures.

In like fashion, relevant government agencies should maintain similar information resources that can be accessed by both companies and consumers and that will provide information concerning regulatory requirements, applicable standards, and data filed in conformity declarations. Companies would easily be able to discover compliance requirements as they prepare products for sale. Consumers will be able to determine the product regulations that may be of concern to them and to determine more easily if filing a complaint with the relevant regulatory authority is justified. Many government agencies already maintain such information resources. Governments that may choose to accept a global framework of principles for conformity assessment should undertake the development and maintenance of related information sources.

Extensive company-maintained databases may be appropriately expected of large manufacturers, many of which already have such a resource. For smaller companies, however, an Internet Web site might provide adequate information and data on their more limited product lines. These databases and Web sites could be linked through Web sites or databases maintained by individual national regulators. A potentially more efficient and useful alternative, however, would be linking multiple sites and databases through a single entity, perhaps a multilateral organization or a nonprofit corporation.

## Other Considerations

Abolition of pre-entry approval could raise concerns that the costs and challenges of after-entry surveillance may increase and that such costs will not be borne directly by manufacturers and suppliers, as is case in *ex ante* approval systems. Regulators should bear in mind that *ex post* regulation will reduce enforcement activities to only what is deemed necessary to address market participants who appear to violate regulations. Active regulatory oversight of all market participants should not be necessary.

*Ex post* market surveillance would allow greater flexibility to manufacturers and suppliers while it allows government intervention when necessary to enforce regulation. For developing countries, after-entry market surveillance should be particularly important. In most of these countries, public resources are severely constrained. Reliance on *ex post* surveillance would reduce regulatory expenditures by focusing government intervention and attendant costs on the policing of violators.

This focused regulation should entail lesser, not greater, cost. Moreover, governments are free to exact fees from all participants at the filing of conformity declarations or product registration. Where products are imported into a given market, a surcharge payable at the time that customs are collected can be earmarked to offset regulatory costs. An alternative approach would be an annual fee paid by market participants to support the regulatory agency responsible for market surveillance; such an arrangement exists for numerous regulatory agencies within the United States at both the state and federal levels. In any case, reduction in fee-specific revenues is likely to be more than recouped through increased sales taxes collected as the IT product market expands, stimulated by increased consumer choice and lower prices.

# Profiles of Chile, Australia, New Zealand, and Taiwan

## Chile

### Organizations

In Chile, technical regulations are issued by various government ministries. These regulations may be promulgated through decrees, supreme decrees, resolutions, or exempt resolutions as specified in legislation. In the case of telecommunications equipment, the regulating agency is the Subsecretaria de Telecomunicaciones; it dictates mandatory standards through a series of decrees. No single agency, however, regulates IT equipment. Various ministries can issue regulations in keeping with their individual ministerial responsibilities. IT equipment that connects to the public telecommunications network, however, is regulated by the subsecretaria.

Technical regulations can be adopted by the regulatory authority on its own initiative or by petitioning parties interested in issuance of a regulation. In the latter case, regulations are proposed to the subsecretaria and it, in turn, makes a decision. In the case of telecommunications equipment, technical regulations are limited to protection of the public network.

National Standardization Institute (INN) is the only standards agency and it promulgates standards for all technologies. It is a private foundation created by the Corporation to Promote Production (CORFO) and is linked to the government through CORFO for its administration. INN works directly with each ministry relative to its respective jurisdiction or operations, but telecommunications standards are established and enforced directly by the subsecretaria.

INN is a member of the ISO. It participates in several regional accreditation forums such as the Asia Pacific Legal Metrology Forum (APLMF), the Pan American Commission onTechnical Standards (COPANT), the Pacific Area Standards Congress (PASC), and the InterAmerican Metrology System (Sistema Interamericano de Metrologia [SIM]).

### Standards

Current standards are intended to not encumber free operation of the markets and free trade, to provide for nondiscriminatory treatment between national and foreign products, and to use international standards as their basis. In Chile there are approximately 2,000 technical standards whose observance is voluntary. No mandatory standards apply to IT products. The voluntary standards are based on criteria accepted by the ISO or IEC (International Electrotechnical Commission).

Most of the subsecretaria's regulations comply with the ITU's telecommunications framework. Within this framework, and because Alcatel was the first large provider in the market, most standards comply with European norms. Despite possible additional costs that foreign equipment manufacturers may incur in order to comply with these standards, the goal of these decrees seems to be the protection of the public telephone network instead of the building of nontrade barriers in favor of local producers. In this regard, Chile's willingness to comply with international standards seems to be a consequence of the lack of large domestic manufacturers of telecommunications and IT equipment in its mainstream markets.

## Accreditation and Testing

The process of conformity assessment is made up of compulsory requirements set by the minister of transport and telecommunications and the under secretary of telecommunications as well as some voluntary systems, such as that administered by INN. In certifying testing laboratories within the telecommunications sector, the subsecretaria does not use international norms such as ISO/IEC; the accreditation of laboratories is ultimately discretionary. Nevertheless, authorizations seem to be based on certain objective parameters—the number and quality of testing machines and the laboratory's history, for example—defined by the subsecretaria's bureaucracy.

Certification is regulated by government decrees or by agreements signed with foreign governments. Despite the fact that Chile has already signed several trade agreements with different countries and free trade zones, mutual recognition agreements addressing testing laboratories for most countries have not yet been finished. Chile has agreements with countries such as Bolivia (1993), Colombia (1994), Canada (1997), Ecuador (1995), Mexico (1998),and Venezuela (1993) and with economic zones such as *Mercado Común del Sur* (MERCOSUR, the Common Market of the South; 1996) and the European Union (EU; it has yet to be signed by the EU member countries.) The treaties with Canada and Mexico appear to be the most advanced regarding mutual recognition of each other's testing facilities.

The certification process includes the participation of various certifying entities, both national (universities and private laboratories) and transnational (Bureau Veritas, Societé General de Surveillance, Lloyd Register, among others). Chile is implementing a voluntary national system for quality certification of products for export. In addition, INN is consolidating at the national level the accreditation system for entities that certify products, for testing laboratories, and for the certification of quality systems as stipulated in ISO 9000. This change does not yet include any norm related to telecommunications equipment or related IT; those are likely to remain under the sole authority of the subsecretaria. The accreditation system is based on international criteria recommended by the ISO and the IEC and on the model established by the EU through the EN 45000 standards.

## Declaration of Conformity

Chile does not accept general criteria for supplier's declaration of conformity (SDOC).

# Australia and New Zealand

## Regulatory Authorities

The Australian Communication Authority (ACA) is the regulatory agency responsible for regulating telecommunications and radiocommunications in Australia. The ACA was established under the Australian Communications Authority Act of 1997 and exercises its power under the Telecommunications Act of 1997 and the Radiocommunications Act of 1992.

ACA's mandate is to promote practical industry self-regulation and to manage "efficient and flexible" access and use of the radio-frequency spectrum. Self-regulation is encouraged through the development of voluntary codes and technical standards by the communications industry. ACA has the power to request that codes be developed and to determine and enforce mandatory standards. ACA has responsibilities for setting technical standards for IT and telecommunications customer premise equipment (CPE) in order to protect the integrity of communications networks, ensure interoperability in the case of the standard telephone service, and address health and safety issues such as human exposure to electromagnetic radiation. ACA represents Australia's communications interests internationally through its participation in the International Telecommunications Union and other bodies.

In New Zealand, EMC and safety requirements for IT and telecommunications equipment are administered by the Ministry of Commerce. The Radio Spectrum Management Group, part of the Operation and Risk Management Branch of the Ministry of Commerce, handles EMC matters.

## Industry Organizations

The Australian Communications Industry Forum (ACIF) has been established by industry to support the self-regulation process. ACIF membership is open and includes carriers, service providers, and user and consumer groups.

Information Technology Association of New Zealand (ITANZ) is the New Zealand national association of organizations involved in the development, production, marketing, and support of goods and services related to the processing of information. Its members include suppliers of computing and telecommunications equipment, suppliers and developers of software, providers of professional and educational IT services, network operators, and providers of value-added services. ITANZ membership is open to all New Zealand companies that supply IT products and services in the computing and telecommunications industries.

## Standards Bodies

Standards Australia is the trading name of the Standards Association of Australia, the leading standards body in Australia. It is an independent, nonprofit association formed in 1922. It has the exclusive right to publish Australian standards and to use the term "Australian Standard" because of a trademark registered to the organization. Through a 1988 memorandum of understanding, the Australian government acknowledges Standards Australia as the primary standards-writing body and recognizes it as Australia's representative on the key international bodies such as the ISO and IEC.

Standards Australia's standards are written by 1,400 technical committees in which more than 9,400 volunteer experts participate. Standards Australia determines the composition of the committees; members are drawn from relevant sectors of industry, government, professional associations, and academia.

Standards Australia follows accepted international guidelines on how standards should be written. Once the validity of a request for a standard has been established, a technical committee drafts the standard. Standards Australia has final approval of standards prepared by the committees through action by the council or by the relevant standards policy board acting on behalf of the council.

Standards New Zealand (SNZ) is an independent, nonprofit organization operating as a part of the New Zealand Standards Council. SNZ provides standards for use in most manufacturing sectors. Standards are developed through an open process of consultation and consensus in which all interested parties are invited to participate. These standards are voluntary guidelines, but they become mandatory if cited in regulations or contracts. SNZ has a technical-help-for-exporters service and operates the New Zealand enquiry point for WTO information on regulations, standards, and certification requirements in overseas markets.

## Accreditation Organizations

In 1991 the two governments agreed to the establishment of the Joint Accreditation System for Australia and New Zealand (JAS-ANZ). Its role is to accredit organizations that conduct conformity certification in both countries. It has the authority to accredit bodies that certify quality management systems, product conformance, and personnel and, also, to accredit laboratory accreditation bodies.

JAS-ANZ is an intergovernmental, nonprofit organization managed by a governing council of 21 members appointed by the two national governments on a two-thirds–one-third basis. The members are drawn from various industry associations, standards and certification interests, and government agencies. An executive committee has been appointed by the council to assist in the development of the accreditation programs, provide management oversight of the Council's operations between meetings, and monitor budget performance.

The National Association of Testing Authorities (NATA) is Australia's only nationally and internationally recognized provider of laboratory accreditation. NATA is the world's largest association of accredited laboratories, with more than 2,500 accredited members. NATA is an independent private company and its operations are monitored and reviewed by its members and by the industry, government, and professional bodies whose representatives make up NATA's council.

NATA's accreditation programs fall into three categories: accreditation of testing laboratories, accreditation of calibration laboratories, and accreditation of inspection services. NATA publishes a range of technical and information publications that cover laboratory practice and evaluation. It promotes its members through publication of an annual directory of accredited laboratories and through advertising, conferences, and related promotional activities.

NATA is one of the founding members of the International Laboratory Accreditation Cooperation (ILAC), the world's principal forum for the international exchange of ideas regarding laboratory accreditation. ILAC investigates the effectiveness of mutual recognition agreements, the development and application of international accreditation criteria, and the promotion of the objectives of laboratory accreditation. NATA also participates in the Organization for Economic Cooperation and Development (OECD) panel on good laboratory practice as well as various international standards committees, including ISO/CASCO (Committee on Conformity Assessment) and ISO/REMCO (the ISO policy committee on reference materials).

International Accreditation New Zealand (IANZ), formerly known as Telarc Ltd., is the national authority for the accreditation of testing and calibration laboratories, radiology services, inspection bodies, and other technical professional services. IANZ was established under the Testing Laboratory Registration Act of 1972 and is a nonprofit government agency, funded from client fees.

Accreditation is achieved after IANZ has assessed the competence of a testing organization and its staff against the technical and management system criteria. To maintain the highest professional standards, accredited organizations are assessed annually. Accredited services carry the distinctive IANZ logo with a specific accreditation service symbol. The logo is recognized in New Zealand by regulatory authorities, users, and consumers.

IANZ operates according to ISO standards. The New Zealand government participates in several international cooperations, such as ILAC, International Laboratory Forum (ILF), Pacific Accreditation Cooperation (PAC), and European Cooperation for Accreditation (EA). IANZ, like NATA, was a founding member of ILAC. The accreditation authorities in Europe, the Asia-Pacific, the United States, and South Africa accept laboratory reports and certificates bearing an IANZ accreditation logo. This recognition is secured by formal MRAs. IANZ has MRAs with more than 20 national authorities.

IANZ and NATA both participate in a regional laboratory accreditation forum, the Asia-Pacific Laboratory Accreditation Cooperation (APLAC). The objectives of APLAC are to help develop and harmonize the procedures and practices of laboratory and inspection accreditation organizations in the region. APLAC was formalized in 1995 when 16 Asia-Pacific bodies, including IANZ and NATA, signed a memorandum of understanding.

## Standards

Requirements are generally based on Australia–New Zealand joint standards (AS/NZS) that are largely compatible with international standards such as ISO/IEC, International Special Committee on Radio Interference (CISPR), or European Telecommunications Standards Institute (ETSI) requirements.

In Australia, ACA introduced the EMC framework (EMCF). EMCF was developed for achieving effective control of electromagnetic interference (EMI) through supplier responsibility. On January 1, 1997, the EMCF became mandatory for the commercial, residential, and light industry products. The primary responsibility for EMCF compliance rests with ACA.

To establish compliance with the EMCF, suppliers have to demonstrate that products meet relevant standards before they put the products on the market. To assure compliance, suppliers must satisfy four basic requirements: they must establish sound technical grounds for product compliance, make and hold a DOC, prepare and keep a compliance folder, and label the product with the C-Tick mark. (A discussion of this follows on page 33.) When these requirements are satisfied, a supplier can offer the product for sale.

Accountability for compliance with the EMCF rests with the supplier, who must take responsibility for products placed on the market. The supplier's responsibility does not end with the sale of the product. Downstream modifications may be made by service and repair people, but they have no obligation to comply with the EMC standards.

Emissions standards are derived from CISPR/IEC standards and with a few exceptions—AS/NZS 3548 (EMC for IT equipment)—are almost identical to CISPR 22 and EN 55022. The exception refers to the conducted line voltage, and, because of this exception, AS/NZS 3548 must be the referenced standard for products to be sold in Australia.

ACA requires compliance with emissions standards, but, except for some medical devices, no immunity requirements are mandatory for products to be sold in Australia. The Australian EMCF is virtually identical to European emissions requirements. Consequently, only immunity tests need to be performed on equipment built to those European standards once compliance with the Australian framework has been established. The European EMC directive imposes broadly based electromagnetic emissions and immunity standards.

In New Zealand, the relevant standard for EMC is AS/NZS 3548 (equal to CISPR 22). Compliance to either Class A (commercial) or Class B (domestic) is mandatory for products to be used in domestic markets. The relevant safety standard is AS/NZS 3260 (equal to IEC 950). Compliance with safety requirements is mandatory. There is no requirement to file compliance papers with any regulatory body. The general framework for testing electrical products is AS/NZS 4417, parts 1–3.

As of January 1999, a new Australia–New Zealand joint framework for EMC came into force. The former separate processes will continue to be an option for certain products, mainly those sold in very small quantities. Under the new joint framework, the two countries are creating a centralized database that will improve and expedite the control, auditing, and registration of suppliers. With this system, suppliers need only register once in either country.

In both countries, safety standards are generally joint Australia–New Zealand standards, mostly based on IEC standards. There are differences in the electrical safety regulatory requirements between Australia and New Zealand; there are also detailed differences among the Australian states. However, AS 4417 provides a harmonized framework for suppliers to establish a basis for claiming compliance with regulators that is equally acceptable in both countries. Until fully harmonized, a manufacturer must comply with the requirements of both countries if the regulatory compliance mark (RCM), a registered trademark, is to be used in both. The conditions for use of the RCM are set out in a standard, AS/NZS 4417.

Although no performance or health requirements apply to IT or telecommunications equipment in New Zealand, both are required to conform to one of the following:

- Federal Communications Commission (FCC) Code of Federal Regulations (CFR) 47, Part 15, relating to digital devices (United States)

- CISPR 22 (International)

- EN 55022 (Europe)

- AS/NZS 3548 (CISPR 22) (EMC) (Australia–New Zealand)

- AS/NZS 3260 (IEC 950) (Safety) (Australia–New Zealand)

CISPR 22, EN 55022, and AS/NZS 3548 are virtually identical; FCC part 15 is somewhat different because it calls up an ANSI specification.

## Accreditation and Testing

In New Zealand, a laboratory can be approved and included on the Ministry of Commerce's list of approved laboratories if that the laboratory is formally registered with its resident country's accreditation scheme for tests relevant to the products to be declared in New Zealand, if the accreditation scheme is formally recognized by IANZ, or if the laboratory provides alternative evidence that satisfies the ministry.

For the first option, a copy of the laboratory's accreditation is required. Evidence for the second option must include, as a minimum,

- a document providing an overview of the laboratory instrument calibration management program from a quality manual (demonstrating that a calibration program is in existence for the relevant instruments);

- documentation that shows the laboratory is demonstrably independent of the organization that has manufactured the item being tested;

- a relevant sample test report, including all test figures and measurement uncertainties;

- a radiated emissions test site attenuation plot and ambient noise plot; or

- a document providing a detailed description of the laboratory quality management system.

Laboratories from which test reports are already accepted may be approved if sufficient evidence has been provided previously. Approval requires re-evaluation every two years.

A supplier must select testing facilities in order to ensure that EMC compliance is achieved. The ministry does not recommend particular testing facilities because of vastly differing costs and testing levels required for the range of products. Manufacturer's testing is allowed for all types of equipment. If suppliers do not have their own accredited laboratory, they must use such a laboratory after doing prototype testing.

If the production volume of electronic devices is sufficiently low and there is a minimal widespread effect from the devices, these devices are termed low-volume devices and are excluded from the EMC framework. Prototypes are implied as low-volume devices. Trade samples are excluded from the framework because the cost of testing a sample product before it is going to be supplied in New Zealand would be unreasonable and would constitute a significant barrier to trade. Kit-set or self-assembled products are also excluded because the manual assembly and use of different assembly techniques effectively makes each kit set a unique product. Customized or individually modified equipment is effectively deemed to be low-volume devices and, thus, is excluded.

The New Zealand government uses ISO/IEC Guide 25 to authorize laboratories for accreditation. Requirements for testing bodies will be fully harmonized between Australia and New Zealand, making any competent facilities acceptable. A new version, which is more extensive and which includes most of the requirements of the revision to Guide 25, now applies.

Test locations are usually not important if the testing organization is accredited to ISO/IEC Guide 25 by the relevant national accreditation body and if IANZ has an MRA with that body. The New Zealand regulators will accept the test results of such organizations in most cases. In New Zealand, there are three types of accreditation bodies: IANZ, test facilities that meet the requirements of accreditation bodies having memorandums of understanding with IANZ or NATA, and 22 other bodies in other countries with which IANZ has an MRA.

The low-volume threshold is currently ten devices in New Zealand; in Australia it is just one. Negotiations between the Ministry of Commerce and ACA are being held in 1999 to determine if the threshold could be set at two devices.

In 1993, concern arose among suppliers that the New Zealand requirement of three test samples of nonradio products was in excess of that required by other countries. The government amended the radiocommunications interference notice to require only one sample of a product.

Under Australian requirements, before actual testing for laboratory accreditation is conducted, the manufacturer must supply the test house with a well-documented EMC test plan. This requirement is designed to expedite testing, enhance repeatability, and minimize testing costs. An initial visit by NATA staff helps prepare a laboratory for accreditation and makes it possible for the laboratory to ask questions about the process. When the laboratory is ready for evaluation, a team of technical assessors is organized in consultation with the laboratory. Depending on the size of the laboratory and the range of testing, the assessment team consists of one to four technical assessors and a NATA staff officer.

The accreditation process involves a thorough evaluation of all the elements of a laboratory, including staffing, training, supervision, quality control, equipment, recording, and reporting of test results and the environment in which the laboratory operates. The evaluation process takes from one to several days and involves the use of specialist technical assessors who evaluate the specific types of testing or measurement. At the end of the assessment, a detailed report is presented to the laboratory showing any areas that require attention and corrective action before being recommended for accreditation. a NATA-endorsed report gives the highest confidence in technical competency and reliability of the results.

Laboratories are accredited when they comply with ISO 17025 (ISO/IEC Guide 25), "General Requirements for the Competence of Testing and Calibration Laboratories." Accredited inspection services must comply with ISO 17020 (EN 45004), "General Criteria for the Operation of Various Types of Bodies Performing Inspection."

Once accredited, a laboratory is re-evaluated periodically to ensure its continued compliance with requirements. A laboratory is also required to participate in relevant proficiency testing programs between reassessments. After receiving NATA accreditation, laboratories are entitled to apply the NATA endorsement to their test and calibration reports. The endorsement is recognized in Australia and other countries as a symbol of testing competence. There is no limit on test locations. Suppliers use test results from a NATA-accredited laboratory or MRA partner laboratory overseas.

NATA-accredited test houses have been thoroughly evaluated by NATA and accredited as meeting internationally recognized standards for good laboratory practice such as the availability of the necessary test facilities, an adequate level of technical competence, and the appropriate quality management systems.

NATA uses ISO/IEC Guide 39 as rules for inspection bodies. NATA-accredited facilities meet the requirements of ISO Guide 25, demanding full calibration traceability of measurement equipment to the national standards of the National Measurement Laboratories (NML) of the Commonwealth Scientific and Industrial Research Organisation (CSIRO). Calibration traceability is essential for the acceptance and recognition of test reports.

When a product is too large or impossible to test, a technical construction file (TCF) should be submitted to an ACA-recognized competent body for assessment. Input/output devices, internal disk drives, memory expansion modules, CPU boards, and power supplies cannot be tested separately. These types of devices must be tested in the system, and this system must be found compliant.

## Declaration of Conformity

Under the EMCF in Australia, a product should be covered by an SDOC. The specification of conformity includes a reference to mandatory standards that have been applied to the product. It must also include reference to any other specifications relevant to product conformity. These may include reference to any quality management system or quality control system that can establish reasonable grounds for accepting consistency of production output with the sample tests. They may also include any supplier's specifications for the purpose of ensuring product conformity through the correct use, operation, installation, interconnection, and maintenance of the device.

The DOC must be completed and held in Australia by the supplier responsible for the product. For imported products, the Australian importer or Australian agent for an overseas supplier should complete the DOC. Supporting evidence is also held by the supplier for purposes of any audit. After compliance is established, a DOC is prepared and placed in a compliance folder. The C-Tick mark is affixed to the product before marketing. There is no need to submit products or any documentation to the ACA for testing or certification before marketing.

When changes are made to computer components, such as circuit board design or power suppliers, the supplier can market the personal computer without the need for a further DOC, provided that the alternative component has been shown to meet the relevant standard. However, modifications to a computer that involve a substantive change will require a new DOC. A peripheral to a personal computer, if sold separately, is subject to a separate DOC. However, if the product is merely a variant and is electrically similar to another tested product, there will be no need for further tests.

The CF should contain the test reports, statements of compliance, a declaration of conformity, and other relevant information. Suppliers do not have to keep two compliance folders, one for EMC and one for telecommunications requirements; one folder holding all relevant information for each framework is acceptable. Also suppliers do not have to make two declarations of conformity, such as one for EMC and one for telecommunications requirements; one declaration of conformity is sufficient for both frameworks. The CF can comprise up to five main elements:

- test reports or TCF,

- a signed SDOC,

- a description of the apparatus, including a photograph and/or block diagram,

- reference to specifications for conformity, and

- a technical description of the apparatus.

Except for the DOC, which must be held in Australia, the other elements of the CF may be held outside Australia after they have been examined and the DOC made. For audit purposes, within 10 working days all contents of the CF must be accessible to the supplier responsible for placing the product on the Australian market. Penalties may apply when a CF is not made available or is incomplete at the time of audit.

NATA-endorsed reports are accepted as technical grounds for making a DOC by the following international bodies:

- Europe: NAMES, STLAG, DANK, SWEDE, SIGNAL, COFRAC RELE, ICLAB, FINAS, NA, SAS

- Australia: NATAAUSTEL

- United States: NVLAP, A2LA, FCC Parts 15 and 18

- NZ: IANZ

The manufacturer or importer of any electrical equipment sold in New Zealand is deemed to have made a self-declaration of compliance with safety standards at the time of offering the product for sale. Supplier DOC is conducted on an individual product basis. The DOC must be based on a compliant test report from a test house that is recognized by the Ministry of Commerce. The organization marketing the product is required to file a DOC with the ministry. After a DOC is filed, the ministry responds with an acknowledgment (not an approval). The vendor has the obligation to prove compliance in the event of an incident or complaint.

Under the new joint EMC scheme, a product that has been declared for one country will be deemed to comply for both. A DOC will be deemed complete only when the specified documentation is held by the vendor. The documentation required is more comprehensive than the former New Zealand requirement for a test report; it now includes block schematics and color photos of the product. A declaration is to be retained by the importer or manufacturer and does not have to be submitted to the Spectrum Management Agency. Instead, a supplier is now required to label its product with the C-Tick mark, as in Australia.

For suppliers who only wish to sell within New Zealand and for whom the labeling option is unattractive, the choice of registering a DOC with the ministry is still be available. A declaration fee is payable for each declaration registered. The registration option exists to recognize concerns that the cost of labeling may be greater in some circumstances; however, the MRA does not apply and unlabeled products will not be able to be sold in Australia.

New Zealand accepts the general criteria for SDOC, ISO/IEC Guide 22. A supplier using DOC is required to be keep the declaration in a CF. The folder will contain the product EMC test results and also circuit diagrams, pictures, and descriptions of the product and any other engineering assessment relevant to the declaration. For products manufactured in New Zealand or Australia, it is permissible for the folder, but not for the declaration, to be held outside Australia. If so, the folder location must be identified on the declaration. The contents of a CF must be made available for inspection for a period of 10 years after a product ceases production or importation.

The TCF is available to suppliers where it is impracticable to use the CF to demonstrate compliance. To use the TCF route, suppliers must apply to a competent body for a technical report. Examples of the use of a TCF include the following:

- Devices on which testing is impractical because of the physical characteristic of the device or because of its location,

- Devices that are marketed as a number of variants, or

- Devices where standards have been applied in part only.

A TCF is prepared in three parts. The first part is prepared by the supplier and comprises claims by the supplier for product conformity and supporting evidence. Such evidence might include the make and mode and also information on the use, installation, and construction of the device. This part must be accompanied by a statement from the supplier, declaring that there is no outstanding application to another competent body with respect to the device. The second part is an inspection report, completed by a competent body, verifying the claims in the draft TCF. The third part is the SDOC. The completed TCF should contain

- an adequate description of the device to be marketed under the TCF;

- a technical rationale for the use of the TCF route;

- a statement of the steps taken to manage the emissions characteristics of the device, including reference to standards applied in part or in full;

- all technical reports relevant to the product;

- any reports issued by the competent body; and

- a DOC.

The current system has different levels of conformity for products based on the products' potential to cause interference. A level 0 product is defined as any electrical or electronic product that does not contain one or more of the following components:

- switched-mode power supply,

- electronic transformer or lighting ballast,

- commutator or slip-ring motor,

- microprocessor or other clocked digital device,

- broadcast service local oscillator,

- ISM RF generator as defined in CISPR 11 (AS/NZS 2064), or

- motor speed controller.

Level 0 products do not require labeling or a DOC; however, they are required to meet the appropriate standard. Testing to ascertain compliance is not necessarily required if an engineering assessment has been made to the effect that the product will not cause interference.

The policy for control of interference from computer equipment and components was adopted in 1993. Key provisions are

- a computer sold as a complete unit is declared as a complete unit;

- a supplier may exchange components such as the motherboard or power supply without making a further DOC, provided the alternate components are demonstrated to have met required standards when tested in a representative host;

- a peripheral is subject to a separate declaration of conformity; and

- suppliers of modular computer systems may make a DOC for combinations of their CPUs, power supplies, and cases and interchange these components in their own, declared products without making a further DOC.

Components that are sold individually do not need a DOC but must have been shown to comply with the required standard when tested in a representative host. Peripherals require a separate declaration. Devices such as a mouse or a joystick that contain only nondigital circuitry or simple converters are viewed as passive add-on devices. Separate compliance is not required for this type of device.

If a change is made to a declared product, the supplier of the product must consider the effect this might have on the interference emissions from the product. Having made a declaration, the supplier is responsible for ensuring that the product continues to comply with the standard.

The declaration may cover a single model or models that are electrically similar. If more than one model is included in a declaration, a detailed description of the basis of this decision is required as well as a list of included models. This option generally covers cosmetic changes or minor upgrades such as increased hard-disk capacity. Even if it is a cosmetic change that does not require a new declaration, notification is required in the event a product is referred to by a different model number. A new DOC is required if a substantive change is made to the product. Examples of such changes are bus architecture, clock frequency, or the physical case.

## Labeling and Audit Systems

In Australia, the C-Tick mark indicates EMC/radiocommunications compliance. The C-Tick and supplier identification identify the person marketing a product in Australia. An Australian distributor must register with the ACA to use the mark. To keep the regulation simple, the supplier is only required to register one application with the ACA to use the C-Tick mark for new products. For EMC compliance, the C-Tick mark must be accompanied by

- the registered name and address of the place of business of the Australian supplier,

- the Australian Company Number (ACN),

- the supplier code issued by the Spectrum Management Agency (SMA), or

- a trademark/name registered in Australia.

If the trademark/name option is used, registration details of the trademark/name should accompany the application. The compliance label must be arranged so that the C-Tick mark and the supplier identification information are contiguous.

The RCM is described in JAS/ANZ 4417 and can be used in either Australia or New Zealand. The RCM indicates a supplier's claim that a product meets applicable electrical safety requirements under the Electricity Acts and the EMCF under the Radiocommunications Acts. The RCM is not mandatory. Independent third-party certification is not required for using the mark.

All devices that acquire a certificate of suitability for electrical safety compliance will be eligible to use the RCM to denote EMC compliance. ACA and the Ministry of Commerce of New Zealand will accept the RCM as equivalent of the C-Tick. This avoids the need to have a different mark for each regulator. Some devices might not be eligible to use the RCM and should display the C-Tick mark. The RCM is regarded as one of several options to indicate electrical safety compliance (others include certificate numbers and manufacturer codes).

In Australia, the A-Tick mark denotes compliance with the telecommunications requirements. Under the 1997 communications act, equipment that complies with the relevant technical standards must display the A-Tick mark. Registration, for which there is no charge, is required to use the A-Tick. The size of the mark should be 3 mm or 12 points. If the product is too small for a label, the labeling information must be displayed on the packaging. In the case of customer equipment, the labeling information must be included in the documentation that accompanies the equipment. The compliance process is based on self-regulation. An importer or manufacturer is required to:

- have equipment tested for compliance with ACA technical standards,

- establish a compliance folder for the equipment, and

- label the equipment with the A-tick as compliant after advising the ACA of the use of the marking.

After a manufacturer registers to use the A-Tick mark, the ACA will issue a supplier code number. If a supplier already has a code number issued under the EMC framework, it will be the same for telecommunications compliance. The supplier code number is issued to the importer or manufacturer and is used on all equipment imported or manufactured by that applicant. This is one of the means that allows the ACA to identify the importer or manufacturer.

If a supplier is registered to use the C-Tick and holds an AUSTEL or Telecom Australia permit, the supplier does not have to register again to use the A-Tick. If a supplier is eligible to use both the A-Tick and C-Tick, the supplier might have to display both marks. The order of display is of no importance.

The ACA monitors industry self-regulation with a program of random audits as well as with investigation of complaints of interference. When a supplier is selected for audit, ACA will provide written notice of the intention to conduct an audit 10 working days before the scheduled date of the audit. NATA test reports will be used as a benchmark by the ACA in any audit. A report from a body that has an MRA with NATA is also accepted; however, ACA will accept NATA test reports as final in any determination.

The supplier must bear the cost of all necessary technical documentation and must pay for three randomly selected samples of the product to be submitted for evaluation, if they are required, and for the cost of their testing at a NATA test laboratory. The test samples and the NATA test laboratory will be selected by the ACA. The use of NATA testing usually provides protection to the person signing the DOC because the test may be used as a defense in any legal dispute.

The following provide an indication of the actions that might constitute offenses under the EMC framework:

- failing to make a DOC regarding a device;

- knowingly making a false DOC or making one without an adequate technical basis;

- failing to provide and to maintain a CF when required;

- failing to advise a competent body that an outstanding application for a technical report has been lodged with another competent body;

- making a false declaration or statement in connection with an application to a competent body for a technical report;

- using the C-Tick mark without SMA authorization;

- offering a product for sale that is not correctly labeled; and

- using any symbol authorized to denote EMC compliance inconsistent with that authorization.

Under New Zealand requirements, the supplier must affix both the label and the supplier identification code to every product placed for supply or sale. Labeling must occur before a product is placed on the market. The label may be affixed at any stage of the supply chain and should normally be placed on the outside of the product as near as possible to the model number.

If it is not practical because of the size or nature of the product, the label can be placed on the product's labeling, packaging, warranty, or instructions. The label may be placed on any promotional material associated with the product. The label should be durably applied by suitable means, including printing, painting, molding, etching, and engraving. Reproduction should be legible and conform to the specifications for each mark. The label may be reproduced in any size or color as long as its visibility is assured.

On January 1, 1999, labeling for EMC compliance became mandatory. Suppliers can use either the C-Tick mark or the RCM. To use the C-Tick, suppliers are required to register with either the Ministry of Commerce (for New Zealand–based suppliers) or the ACA; it is not necessary to register in both Australia and New Zealand. Suppliers who register in New Zealand will be issued a code number with the prefix Z; suppliers who register in Australia will be issued a code number with the prefix N. Suppliers must complete and retain a DOC, which can be held in either country. When labeled, New Zealand products can be sold legally in Australia and vice versa.

If a computer product meets the requirements of the radiocommunications regulations of 1993, suppliers of computer equipment must use the Ministry of Commerce's communication-friendly label for products that are subject to a DOC.

Other national and international bodies have established proprietary EMC frameworks, some of which include product labeling conditions to indicate compliance. For example, the EU uses a special symbol, CE, to indicate compliance with European ECM standards. Internationally accredited testing laboratories can indicate compliance with a standard by approving the placement of their own mark on a product. However, the New Zealand ministry has several concerns about these labels:

- The labels are used to signify more than EMC compliance (for example, the scope of the CE mark covers areas as diverse as electrical, fire, and health safety);

- Registration of the labels is held outside New Zealand, making control and enforcement of use virtually impossible; and

- Supplier identification is not incorporated nor is it a requirement of the use of these marks.

The ministry therefore cannot be certain that such labels are actually used to signify EMC compliance.

An EMC compliance audit will consist of either an arranged visit to the supplier or the submission of the CF to the ministry. Auditing is based on the DOC and is, therefore, product-based. A single supplier might be audited based on the number of declarations submitted. Policing for safety requirements is mainly based on incidents and complaints reporting.

Random audits are conducted. The vendor might be requested to supply either a compliant test report or a sample for testing by the ministry (the selection of the product and either a test report or a sample is done by the ministry). Although it is a random auditing system, the likelihood of auditing is increased if interference complaints are received about a supplier's products. An audit is almost certain if continued complaints are received. A minimum of 10 days' notice will be given before a visit.

Even if a supplier operates in multiple markets, the frequency of auditing will be the same as if they supplied only one market. The auditing authority will be Ministry of Commerce in New Zealand and the ACA in Australia, depending on the registration location.

In New Zealand, suppliers of computer products are requested to supply only a single sample to the Ministry of Commerce's laboratory for testing. If the product fails the audit test, the party will be given 10 days to rectify the situation. During that period, the supplier will have the option of supplying more samples to be tested, at its own cost, or withdrawing the product from sale immediately. If more products are tested, the test results will be statistically assessed for compliance with the required standard. If they pass, no further action will be required. If they fail to meet the standard again, the supplier will be required to either withdraw the product from sale or make modifications to the product to make it meet the standard and ensure that future stocks are modified as well.

Products already sold will not be compulsorily recalled; however, if a case of interference is traced to such a product, the supplier will be expected to rectify the situation. In extreme cases, the ministry resorts to legal action. Following are options that are open to the ministry if a supplier fails an audit when a product is independently tested as noncompliant:

- Encourage the supplier to seek a solution to the noncompliant design,

- Order the cessation of the sale of the offending items,

- Order the total recall of offending products, or

- Prosecute the supplier.

If a supplier fails an audit owing to insubstantial documentation, no audit fees will be charged. If product testing must be carried out to complete the audit, the cost of that testing will be paid by the supplier.

The ministry's field offices will continue the routine monitoring of compliance at retail outlets by way of monthly surveys spread around the country. Any product found to be not compliant with the regulations will be traced to the supplier and the supplier will be given the opportunity to comply with the declaration process. If the supplier does not conform, the ministry will resort to prosecution. The ministry will not pay for testing to be undertaken for these products because they do not fall within the scope of the audit program.

The ministry's regulations have offense provisions for the sale, use, supply, and possession of products that

- do not comply with the required standard,

- have not had a DOC completed where required,

- are not labeled or registered on the ministry's declaration database,

- are labeled in an incorrect manner, or

- cause interference to radiocommunications services.

It will be an offense for a supplier to:

- be unable to supply a compliance folder for audit purposes,

- make a false declaration of conformity,

- not comply with a written notice from the ministry to cease the sale of a product,

- not comply with a written notice from the ministry to recall a product,

- not provide a sample or samples for testing at a IANZ/NATA-accredited laboratory when requested to do so by the ministry, or

- label a product without being a registered supplier.

The Radiocommunications Act levies a fine not exceeding $30,000 for an individual and $200,000 for a corporation for violation of these regulations.

# Taiwan

## Organizations

Under the Commodity Inspection Act, the Bureau of Commodity Inspection and Quarantine (BCIQ) under the Ministry of Economic Affairs (MOEA) was established as Taiwan's product inspection and regulation agency. The main duties of BCIQ include conducting product inspection to ensure consumer protection, promoting ISO 9000 to assist establishment of quality management systems, and providing other inspection and testing services. BCIQ has headquarters in Taipei with six additional regional offices throughoutTaiwan. BCIQ has formed teams to coordinate construction of test facilities, develop and implement procedures, and review projects.

BCIQ determines standards for design, manufacture, and sale of products that may cause or be affected by electromagnetic interference (EMI). Products determined by MOEA to be subject to inspection must pass BCIQ's inspection before the product is marketed in Taiwan.

The Directorate General of Telecommunications (DGT), under the Ministry of Telecommunications (MOTC), sets policy for the development of the telecommunications sector. Its role is to protect consumers, issue licenses for service providers, ensure technical compatibility and interconnection among service providers, recommend standards, and determine time frames for government clearances and approvals. The Public Telecommunications Department (PTD) is the telecommunications regulatory authority. It defines standards and grants approvals for telecommunications equipment. The PTD is also responsible for inspection of approved or nonapproved terminal equipment and networks and for approval guidelines and documentation review. PTD reports directly to the DGT.

BCIQ has promoted cooperative programs with international testing and certification bodies in order to assist Taiwanese manufacturers in obtaining market entry into importing countries and in competing more successfully in the international market. BCIQ participates in the International Accreditation Forum (IAF) and in the International Auditor and Training Certification Association (IATCA).

BCIQ has also signed cooperative agreements or memorandums of understanding with a number of international inspection or certification organizations. BCIQ also participates in the Pacific Accreditation Cooperation (PAC) and in the Subcommittee on Standards and Conformance (SCSC) under Asia-Pacific Economic Cooperation (APEC).

## Standards

MOEA issues the regulations that govern electromagnetic compatibility and that establish the inspection process for products subject to EMC regulation. The EMC law requires compliance with Chinese National Standard (CNS) 13438. EMC regulation was implemented on January 1, 1998. Taiwan requires that all IT equipment, including computers and peripherals, sold within the country meet emissions requirements. So far, products announced as subject to EMC inspection include copy machines, television sets, videocassette recorders, facsimile machines, and IT equipment. The following categories of products are subject to the EMC requirements:

- Disposable, domestic, and light industry products;

- General electrical appliances, electronic products, and office equipment and supplies;

- Equipment and devices for maintenance and installation;

- Devices for computer information network systems;

- General transportation facilities equipment, including passenger transport vehicles, freight transport vehicles; and

- Large-scale industry products.

Compulsory EMC regulation applies only to emissions. The EMC test is based on CNS 13438—a Chinese-language version of CISPR 22 for IT equipment. The applicable standard for testing is similar to CISPR 22, but radiation testing must be done in 10-meter distances for Class A products. Distances of 3 meters are still acceptable for Class B.

Other standards adopted as EMC regulation are based on internationally harmonized documents—CNS-13439/CISPR 13 and CNS-13306 (similar to CISPR 16 and ANSI C63.4). Because the standard for household appliances (CISPR 14) is currently in draft form, no CNS standard number has been assigned yet.

## Accreditation and Testing

BCIQ undertakes all test performance certifications and approval registrations. Performance certification by Taiwanese testing institutions is compulsory. Operation guidelines for approval and management of designated EMC laboratories are established in accordance with Article 5 of the Regulations Governing the Electromagnetic Compatibility of Commodities. When sample testing is required, model tests by testing departments licensed by BCIQ on the basis of ISO Guide 25 will be compulsory.

Testing departments qualified by BCIQ are periodically assessed as to their qualifications. Laboratories that fail to pass the assessment may apply for a reassessment within two months after receiving the results. There are seven testing institutions at present.

A certificate of approval is valid for three years. Before expiration, relevant documents must be submitted in order to apply for certificate renewal. For the approval of any modifications made to the registered technical categories, an approved laboratory is required to file another application. BCIQ can revoke the registration of an approved laboratory in the event of falsification of test reports. Laboratories that intend to obtain BCIQ approval to conduct EMC testing must file an application form with the following documents:

- Identification of the laboratories,

- Quality manual of the laboratories,

- List of the standard operating procedures,

- Documents related to the calibration traceability system,

- Calibration data of the testing sites, and

- Internal quality audit procedures.

Importers or domestic manufacturers are required to submit their products to the designated EMC laboratories for testing and obtain test reports. BCIQ, not a manufacturer, designates testing institutions to carry out inspection under contract to BCIQ.

BCIQ occasionally requests the applicant to furnish a sample in order to conduct the test. After importers or local manufacturers obtain test reports, they must apply to BCIQ for EMC-type approval by presenting related test reports and other application materials.

An applicant for EMC approval should prepare three copies of the completed application form (in ISO A4 format) and submit them to one of the seven BCIQ offices for initial review. The applicant must keep the samples and related technical documents for later verification.

BCIQ takes three to four weeks to review the application. The application consists of the following materials:

- User manual and specifications in Chinese;

- Desired location of identification number and the manner in which it is to be affixed;

- Blocked diagram;

- Table or list of the EMC components and emissions sources;

- Product catalogue and a color photo, including its appearance and internal structure; and

- An original copy of the EMC test report, in ISO A4 format or equivalent file holder.

For a Class A device, a manufacturer's user manual can be in English, but for a Class B device, a user manual must be in Chinese. Otherwise the application will be rejected. BCIQ does not require schematic diagrams, but a manufacturer must provide functional block diagrams with an indication of the EMI emissions source and suppression component.

The application must be submitted by an authorized representative located in Taiwan. A manufacturer must have an agent in Taiwan deliver the information to the BCIQ offices. Application fees will be charged in accordance with the guideline for the rate of commodity inspection fees. The fees must be paid within the prescribed period.

After receiving an application, the BCIQ local office issues a registration number, not an accreditation number, for the application. The BCIQ office returns one copy of the application form to the applicant, keeps one copy, and forwards one copy to the Inspection Department of BCIQ for examination. After these steps, evaluation of the documentation begins.

If there is a lack of proper documentation, the applicant may be requested to resubmit materials for sample testing purposes. In that case, the applicant should send the requested documents within two months from the date of notification; otherwise the approval will be denied.

If evaluation based on the submitted documents proves difficult, part or all of the items in question might be subjected to retest. For products produced in small quantities, a manufacturer can declare the imported quantity of the product on a lot-by-lot basis to a local BCIQ office.

BCIQ will usually be able to finish applications within three to four weeks. However, if the EMC team requests another sample, the process will take much longer. When certification has been granted, follow-up enforcement will be handled by the BCIQ regional offices.

If a product passes the examination, the local BCIQ office will receive notification to issue the EMC certificate and identification numbers for the products. The certificate is called an accreditation certificate for an electromagnetic wave conforming product. The identification number is called type approval identification number. The number must be included on the product labeling along with other required information.

Accredited products are to be announced in the monthly test report. Certified products can follow the normal procedure for custom clearance and be placed on the market for sale. A rejection notice will be issued in the case of a product that fails to be accredited. In such case, the applicant may apply for a reinspection, free of charge, within 15 days after receiving notification. Reinspection shall be conducted using the original sample. An additional sample will be taken only if nothing remains of the original sample or if the original sample cannot be inspected.

If a laboratory is incompetent to test a product owing to the size of the product or to inadequate facilities, the laboratory can contact BCIQ to lease a larger EMC laboratory in order to conduct proper testing. If a testing sample requires additional relevant peripheral equipment, and such equipment is not in Taiwan, BCIQ might dispatch engineers to go abroad and conduct or witness the testing. If BCIQ decides not to conduct or witness testing abroad, the applicant can submit a specific request for the testing to be conducted by a laboratory accredited by an impartial third-party testing institution.

Testing abroad requires three steps. First, an applicant submits a specific request for the testing to be conducted by a laboratory accredited by an impartial third-party testing institution. The applicant must fill in an application form, attach related inspection and testing technical files on the selected EMC laboratory, and submit them to BCIQ. The technical files include information pertaining to the laboratory's testing and measurement equipment, the calibrated testing site, and other related data. Second, BCIQ will arrange a coordination meeting with the applicant and EMC engineers from the inspection department to discuss whether or not to use these procedural points. Third, BCIQ will notify the applicant about the decision; if accepted, the applicant will also be notified about implementation requirements. All costs incurred, including the cost on traveling abroad, are borne by the applicant. If any modifications are made to the approved design, the products should resubmitted for approval.

A manufacturer applying to register a series product must provide one photocopy of the EMC approval certificate, stating the CCC code, model number, certificate number of the original registered product, and a description of the family series. A manufacturer should also furnish documents on the original type test for review. If necessary, the laboratory might request samples for certain items. BCIQ can collect examination fees in addition to the series product verified charge that is paid to the performing EMC laboratory. The original registered manufacturer shall file the application for the series product. If a manufacturer lost or destroyed its approval certificate, the certificate holder can apply for a replacement certificate.

Accreditation of laboratories is performed in accordance with ISO Guide 25. According to a message found on a discussion board on the Internet, the seven EMC laboratories in Taiwan are in compliance with applicable IEC, CISPR, FCC, and EN specifications as well as with the ISO Guide 25 general requirements for the competence of calibration and testing laboratories.

Manufacturers that want to obtain approval will be required to have their products tested by Taiwanese laboratories. After the U.S. government issued a formal protest to Taiwan to change the implementation of the 1997 EMC law, Taiwan accepted applications from 40 U.S. laboratories for mutual recognition. This mutual recognition extends only to U.S. laboratories accredited by NVLAP or A2LA; Japan and the EU are not included in this arrangement. Because accreditation bodies in the EU do not recognize Taiwan's laboratories, BCIQ will not approve EU laboratories.

Test reports and owner manuals must be in Chinese. An original copy of the test report must be filed in Taiwan.

## Declaration of Conformity

Currently the government does not recognize the SDOC.

## Labeling and Audit System

EMC labeling is compulsory in Taiwan. After products pass inspection, BCIQ will issue an inspection certificate and the supplier must affix approval labels to the packaging of each product. The label for general products to be sold on the domestic market is indicated by the letter C. The certified product is also to be labeled with the accreditation registration number in accordance with the product procedure for EMC model accreditation registration. The number must be affixed with a stamp or an inscription to the body of the product. The applicant must specify the position of the number and the manner in which it is affixed when submitting the application.

Products that might be determined to be safety or health risks or that might be deemed to pose a danger to the public owing to their materials, structure, or use are subject to a mandatory safety mark scheme. To obtain the safety mark, a manufacturer must establish a quality assurance system and have the system assessed and approved by BCIQ. Evaluation consists of inspection of product samples and surveillance of the quality assurance system. The safety mark and a registration number must be affixed to the product that successfully passes inspection. Foreign national inspection bodies can negotiate cooperative inspections with BCIQ through mutual recognition.

BCIQ conducts three types of random audits of the products. First, BCIQ personnel go to factories to perform sample inspections. Second, BCIQ conducts random market audits by purchasing products in various localities for inspection. Third, foreign goods coming in by sea or air might be inspected. In such cases, BCIQ might request a single sample for future testing but allow the remainder of the shipment to be released for distribution. Approved laboratories are also subject to random audits at least once a year; however, the frequency of the audits may be increased.

If an audited product fails random sampling by a designated laboratory, its product certification will be revoked. The manufacturer will be notified to withdraw the product from the market and fines will be levied in accordance with the Commodity Inspection and Quarantine Law.

Approval shall be revoked under any of the following situations:

- Products are not properly labeled and corrective actions are not taken within the specified time period after notification;

- Inspected samples purchased from the market fail to meet inspection standards, and manufacturers of the products in question fail to withdraw the products from the market within the specified time period after notification;

- A certificate holder, without acceptable reason, refuses to allow the inspection authority to take samples for testing;

- A certificate holder, who did not pay required fees, fails to pay the fees within the specified time period after notification; and

- A certificate holder obtains EMC type approval illegally or uses the certificate and label beyond the approved scope.

EMC approval shall be canceled under any of the following situations:

- The certificate holder applies for cancellation,

- The business of a certificate holder is no longer operational, and

- The commodities no longer require EMC approval.

A supplier should return its EMC approval to BCIQ within 30 days after the cancellation or revocation of the approval.

# Glossary

**ACCREDITATION OF LABORATORIES:** process by which a regulatory agency or government authority recognizes the capacity and qualification of laboratories to conduct conformity assessment testing of products.

**AGREEMENT ON TECHNICAL BARRIERS TO TRADE (TBT):** agreement that obligates WTO members to ensure that technical regulations, voluntary standards, and conformity assessment procedures do not create unnecessary obstacles to trade. In accepting the TBT agreement, members agree to ensure that their government standardizing bodies accept and comply with the agreement's code of good practice. Where international standards exist, the code of good practice encourages standardizing bodies to use them.

**AGREEMENT ON TRADE IN BASIC TELECOMMUNICATIONS SERVICES:** agreement on market access for basic telecommunications services concluded by the WTO in February 1997. The offers of 69 governments were annexed to the General Agreement on Trade in Services. The markets of the participants accounted for more than 91 percent of global telecommunications revenues in 1995.

**ASIA PACIFIC ECONOMIC COOPERATION (APEC):** primary intergovernmental vehicle for the promotion of open trade and economic cooperation among the 18 member economies in the Asia-Pacific region.

**ASIA-PACIFIC LABORATORY ACCREDITATION COOPERATION (APLAC):** organization of laboratory accreditation bodies in the Asia-Pacific region. APLAC is one of the specialist regional bodies supporting the trade facilitation activities of the APEC Subcommittee on Standards and Conformance (SCSC).

**ASIA PACIFIC LEGAL METROLOGY FORUM (APLMF):** organization established in 1994 by 14 of the 18 APEC economies to develop mutual confidence among legal metrology authorities in the Asia-Pacific region; identify and promote the removal of technical and administrative barriers to trade in the field of legal metrology; and promote mutual recognition arrangements between members and with other regional groups and individual nations.

**BENCHMARKING:** use of a given set of criteria as a standard against which to measure or evaluate performance.

**CERTIFICATION:** procedure by which a third party gives written assurance that a product, process, or service conforms to specified standards or requirements.

**CERTIFYING AGENTS:** independent organizations that certify the accuracy of tests showing the compliance of a given product with relevant standards or requirements.

COMPLIANCE AUDIT: procedure or evaluation for determining that an organization has complied with applicable legal and regulatory requirements.

COMPLIANCE FOLDER (CF): file in which a supplier or manufacturer places all required information that documents product conformity with specified regulatory requirements; often a CF must be kept in the country of sale.

CONFORMITY ASSESSMENT: process of determining whether products, services, and/or management systems meet relevant requirements for target markets. Conformity assessment typically involves sampling, inspection, evaluation, testing, certification, and registration of products and of quality and environmental management systems. Those products and systems often must meet the approval of and be accredited by laboratories or certifying agents.

CONVERGENCE: act, condition, quality, or fact of approaching the same point from different directions or of tending toward a meeting or intersection. In the communications and IT industries, the term is generally understood to connote the merging of the technologies over which voice, data, video, and multimedia services may be provided.

DECLARATION OF CONFORMITY (DOC): process by which a supplier or manufacturer asserts that its products, systems, or services conform to specified requirements and discloses technical information documenting conformity (also referred to as supplier's or manufacturer's declaration of conformity [SDOC]).

ELECTROMAGNETIC COMPATIBILITY: ability of equipment to function in an electromagnetic environment without generating unacceptable emissions or disturbances.

ELECTROMAGNETIC EMISSIONS: emission of waves of magnetism arising from electrical charge in motion, having both electric and magnetic components.

ELECTROMAGNETIC INTERFERENCE: degradation of equipment performance by electromagnetic emissions or disturbance.

EUROPEAN COOPERATION FOR ACCREDITATION (EA): organization jointly formed by EAC (European Accreditation of Certification) and EAL (European Cooperation for Accreditation of Laboratories). that takes charge of all European conformity assessment activities, including testing and calibration, inspection, certification of management systems, certification of products, and certification of personnel. Members of EA are nationally recognized accreditation bodies of the member countries of the European Union and the European Free Trade Agreement (EFTA).

EX ANTE: Latin term meaning "from before the fact" or "prior to."

EX POST: Latin term meaning "from after the fact" or "subsequent to."

INFORMATION TECHNOLOGY AGREEMENT (ITA): agreement adopted by 40 WTO member states and separate custom territories to eliminate customs and other duties and charges on IT products by January 2000. Six main categories of products are covered by the agreement: computers, telecommunications equipment, semiconductors, semiconductor manufacturing equipment, software, and scientific instruments.

**INTERAMERICAN METROLOGY SYSTEM (SISTEMA INTERAMERICANO DE METROLOGIA [SIM]):** clearinghouse for measurement standards in the region; all metrology organizations in the Americas are involved.

**INTERNATIONAL ACCREDITATION FORUM (IAF):** membership group of accreditation bodies drawn from around the world. The main goals are to exchange information, harmonize members' operating procedures, and maintain IAF multilateral recognition agreements (MRAs) signed by 16 accreditation bodies of different countries.

**INTERNATIONAL AUDITOR AND TRAINING CERTIFICATION ASSOCIATION (IATCA):** organization that addresses the variations among different countries in auditor certification criteria and consequent auditor standards. IATCA has developed a set of criteria governing auditor certifications and auditor training in order to eliminate the need for multiple certifications of auditors and multiple approvals of auditor training courses.

**INTERNATIONAL LABORATORY ACCREDITATION COOPERATION (ILAC):** international cooperation among the various laboratory accreditation schemes operated throughout the world. ILAC provides advice and assistance to countries that are in the process of developing laboratory accreditation systems.

**INTERNATIONAL ORGANIZATION FOR STANDARDIZATION (ISO):** worldwide federation of national standards bodies from 130 countries. It is a nongovernmental organization established in 1947 to promote the development of standardization and related activities to facilitate the international exchange of goods and services. ISO's work results in international agreements that are published as international standards.

**INTERNATIONAL ORGANIZATION OF LEGAL METROLOGY (OIML):** organization established in 1955 to promote global harmonization of legal metrology procedures that has developed a worldwide technical structure that provides its members with metrological guidelines for the elaboration of national and regional requirements concerning the manufacture and use of measuring instruments.

**INTERNATIONAL STANDARDS:** protection by the copyright of an international standards body (e.g., ISO, IEC). The exploitation right of this copyright is automatically transferred to the national standards bodies that compose the membership of ISO or IEC for the purpose of drawing up national standards. Each draft and each published international standard bears a copyright statement with the international copyright symbol, the publisher's name, and the year of publication.

**INTERNATIONAL TRADE COMMISSION (ITC):** independent, quasi-judicial federal agency in the United States that provides objective trade expertise to both the legislative and executive branches of the U.S. government, determines the impact of imports on U.S. industries, and directs actions against trade practices deemed to be unfair. USITC publishes reports on U.S. industries and the global trends that affect them.

**INTEROPERABILITY:** ability of two systems or products to interconnect and operate mutually.

**ISO 9000:** family of standards that represents a set of requirements for quality management systems designed to ensure that an organization can consistently deliver a product or service that meets accepted quality requirements.

**ISO/IEC GUIDE 22:** specific rules that govern a manufacturer's or supplier's declaration of conformity with standards, particularly addressing general conditions, procedure, standardization documents, and user–supplier relations.

**ISO/IEC GUIDE 25:** rules that govern general requirements for the competence of calibration and testing laboratories.

**MARKS:** system of protected marks, applied or issued under the rules of a certification system, to be placed on a product indicating conformity with a specified standard or other normative document.

**METROLOGY:** science of weights and measures or of measurement.

**MOST FAVORED NATION (MFN):** principle that requires WTO members to grant the products of suppliers of any other member state the best treatment granted to comparable products of suppliers of any other country, whether or not the latter is a member of the WTO. This obligation guarantees that any liberalization steps, whether negotiated bilaterally or applied unilaterally, will be extended to all members. Although it does not, by itself, require any particular degree of market openness, it supports fair competition among trading partners.

**MUTUAL RECOGNITION AGREEMENT (MRA):** agreement (in the context of conformity assessment) that contemplates the mutual acceptance by two or more governments and relevant private sector stakeholders of their respective conformity assessment procedures or requirements.

**ONE-STOP SHOPPING:** euphemistic phrase that describes the practice of obtaining conformity approval in one country and having that approval accepted in all others.

**PACIFIC AREA STANDARDS CONGRESS (PASC):** forum for executives of Pacific regional standards bodies; it also supports development of consolidated positions to both ISO and IEC.

**PAN AMERICAN COMMISSION ON TECHNICAL STANDARDS (COPANT):** nonprofit association that promotes the development of technical standardization and related activities. The commission coordinates the activities of all standardization institutes in Latin American countries and develops all types of product standards, standardized test methods, terminology, and related matters.

**SELF-DECLARATION OF CONFORMITY:** procedure by which a supplier or manufacturer gives written assurance in the form of a standardized document that a given product, process, or service conforms to the specified requirements.

**SELF-TESTING:** process by which manufacturers test their own products for conformity with specified regulatory requirements, notably standards.

**STANDARDS:** rules, guidelines, or requirements intended achieve a common level of conformity or functionality. International standards are established through consensus, approved by an appropriate body or bodies, set up in documents under copyright, and are complied with on a voluntary basis. National standards may be established by a parallel process or may be established by regulatory action by an authorized national body or agency.

**UNILATERAL ACCEPTANCE:** acceptance by a given country, of its own volition or on its own initiative, of the conformity assessment procedures or requirements of another country or other countries; or the acceptance by a given country of a declaration of conformity by a manufacturer or supplier.

**WORLD TRADE ORGANIZATION (WTO):** organization that provides a mechanism that supports the negotiating of multilateral trade agreements that provide the legal rules for international commerce. The agreements are essentially contracts, binding governments to maintain their trade policies within agreed bounds or conditions. The WTO also provides a dispute resolution process through which alleged violations of trade commitments by participating nations can be adjudicated.

# About the Authors

**WILLIAM B. GARRISON JR.** is director of the CSIS International Communications Program. He has served as a consultant to public- and private-sector clients and to foreign governments on industrial restructuring and regulation. Before entering private practice, he was director of the Office of Congressional Relations and Public Affairs for the National Telecommunications and Information Administration at the U.S. Department of Commerce. Garrison holds a B.A. from Duke University and a J.D. from the University of North Carolina.

**PETER S. WATSON** is a senior associate with CSIS. Previously with the U.S. International Trade Commission, he was appointed to the commission by President Bush in 1990 and subsequently named its chair by President Clinton (1994–1996). Prior to his work at the commission, Watson served in the White House as director of Asian Affairs at the National Security Council and as the Overseas Private Investment Corporation special adviser to the president. An adjunct professor at the National Defense University, he holds an LL.M. from McGill University, an LL.B. from Auckland University, and an M.I.B.A. from West Coast University.